Basic

MW00783976

Scales, Chords, Arpeggios & Cadences

Complete For Piano

In All Keys

By Margaret L. White

Basic

Scales, Chords, Arpeggios & Cadences

Table of Contents

The Circle of Fifths

The Circle of Fifths chart, detailed below, is a circular arrangement of the 12 keys in ascending or descending fifths: the sharps arranged from the top moving clockwise (ascending) and the flats arranged from the top moving counterclockwise (descending). The Relative Keys, major and minor keys having the same Key Signature, are shown together on the circle. The keys at the bottom of the circle are the **Enharmonic Keys**, which have the same sound while having two different names.

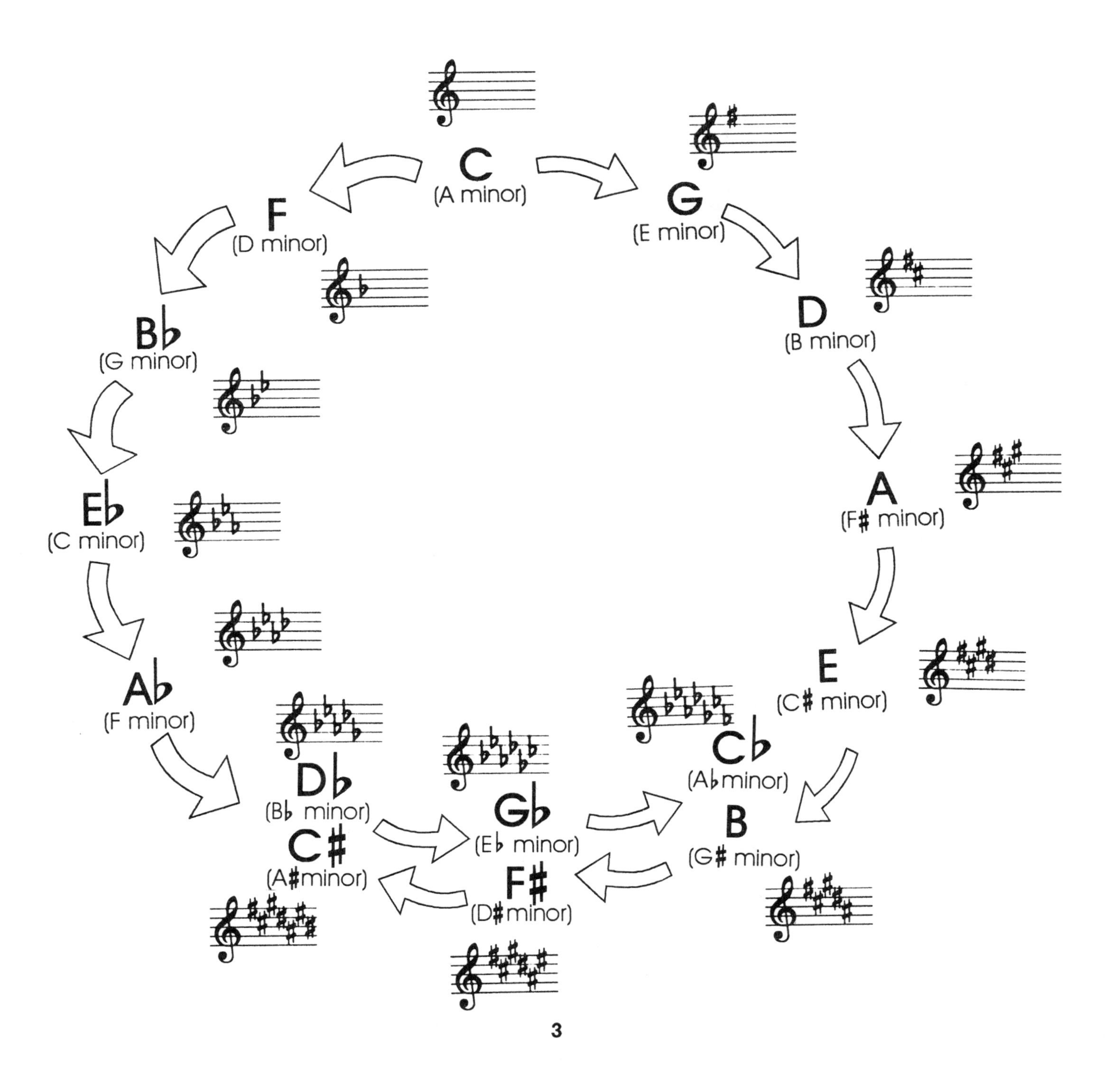

C
(A minor)
G
(E minor)
D
(B minor)
A
(F# minor)
E
(C# minor)
Cb
(Ab minor)
B
(G# minor)
Gb
(Eb minor)
F#
(D# minor)
Db
(Bb minor)
C#
(A# minor)
Ab
(F minor)
Eb
(C minor)
Bb
(G minor)
F
(D minor)

Major Scales

A scale is a series of notes in succession. The Major Scale is built on two whole steps, one half step, three whole steps, and one half step. A Major Scale can start on any note but must always follow the same whole-step, half step... pattern.

C Major Scale

W W H W W W H

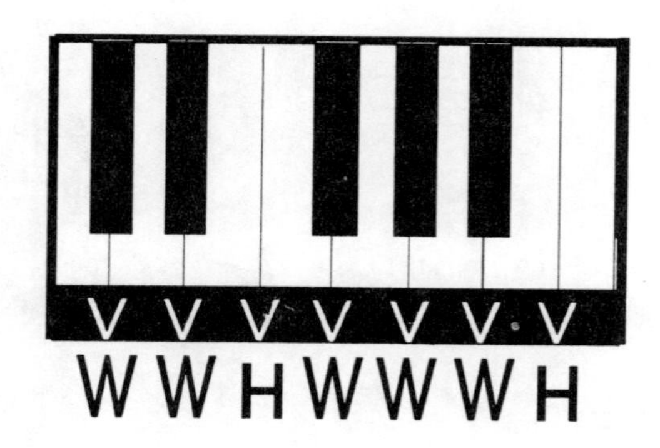
WWHWWWH

Chords

A Chord is three or more notes played simultaneously.

C Major Chord

The **Root** is the note the chord is built on.

A **Major Chord** contains the 1st, 3rd, and 5th notes of a major scale.

Root

An **Inversion** of a chord means to place the bottom note of the chord on the top.

Inversion

The **Tonic** is the first note of a scale.

A **Sub-dominant** is the 4th note of any scale.

A **Dominant** is the 5th note of any scale.

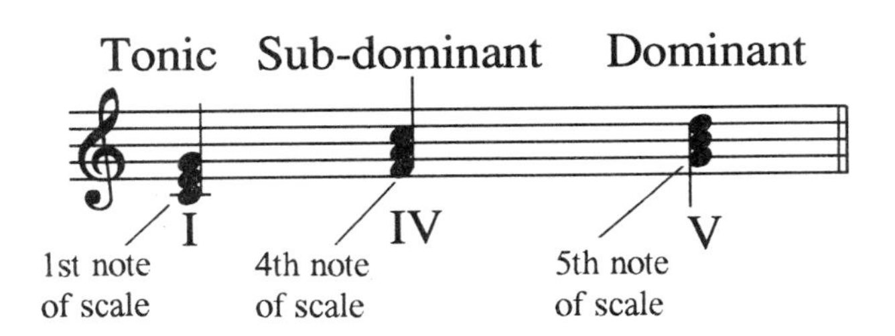
Tonic
Sub-dominant
Dominant
I
IV
V
1st note of scale
4th note of scale
5th note of scale

A **Dominant 7th Chord** is built on the fifth step of any scale, major or minor; consisting of one major third plus two minor thirds.

Cadences

A **Cadence** is a specific pattern of chords.

The **Authentic** cadence is the I (Tonic), V (Dominant), I (Tonic) pattern.

The **Plagal** cadence is the I (Tonic), IV (Sub-dominant), I (Tonic) pattern.

The **Mixed** cadence is the I, IV, (I), V, I pattern.

Authentic
Plagal
Mixed
I V I
I IV I
I IV (I) V I

Arpeggios

An arpeggio is playing the notes of a chord consecutively.

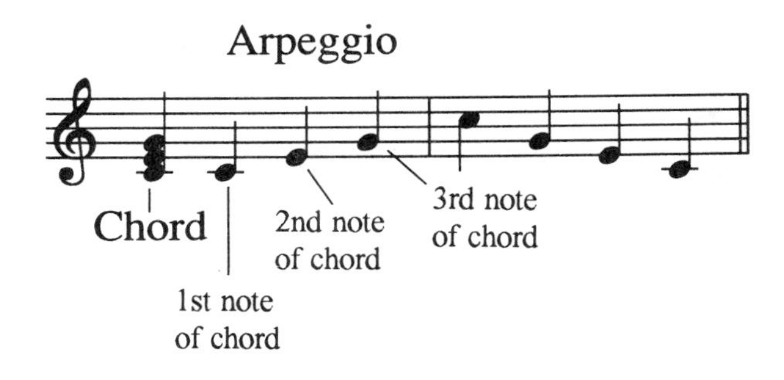
Arpeggio
Chord
1st note of chord
2nd note of chord
3rd note of chord

C Major

C Major Scale (1 Octave)

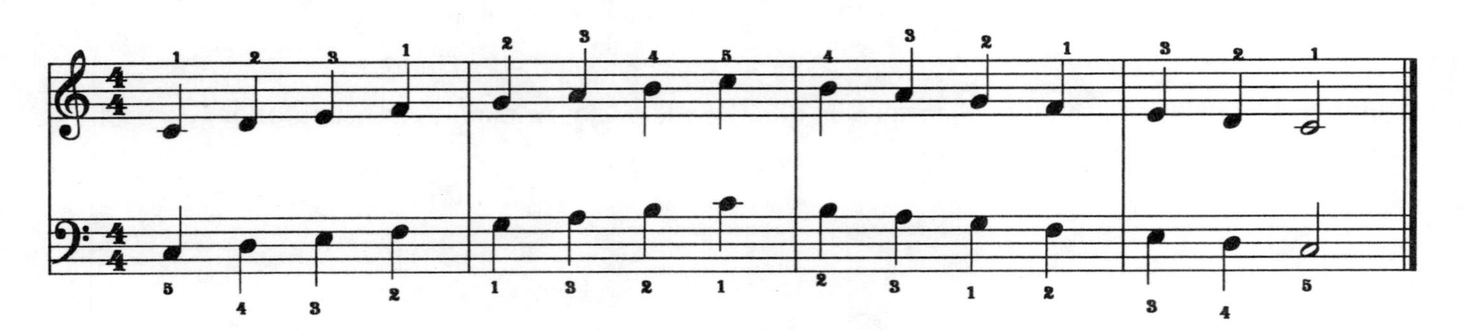

C Major Scale (2 Octaves)

C Major Arpeggio (1 Octave) C Major Arpeggio (2 Octaves)

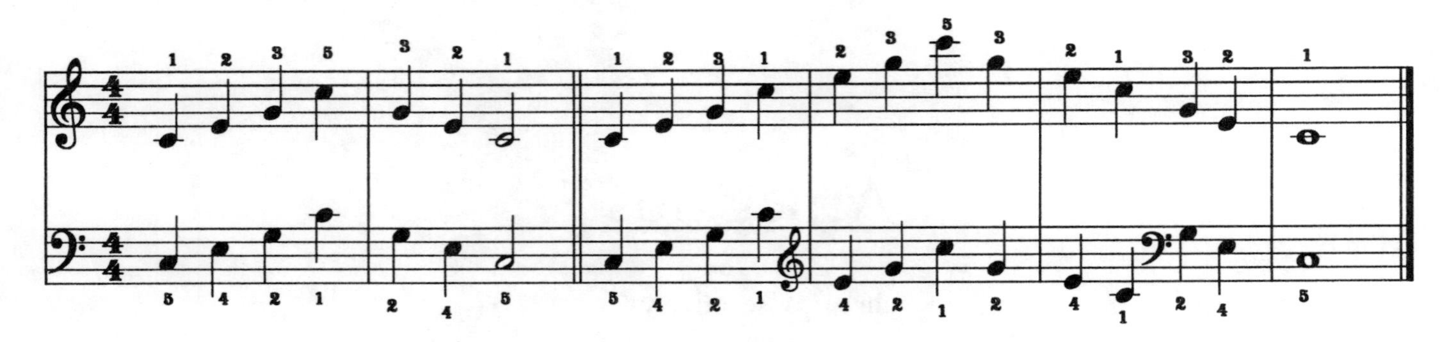

C Major Arpeggios In Inversions

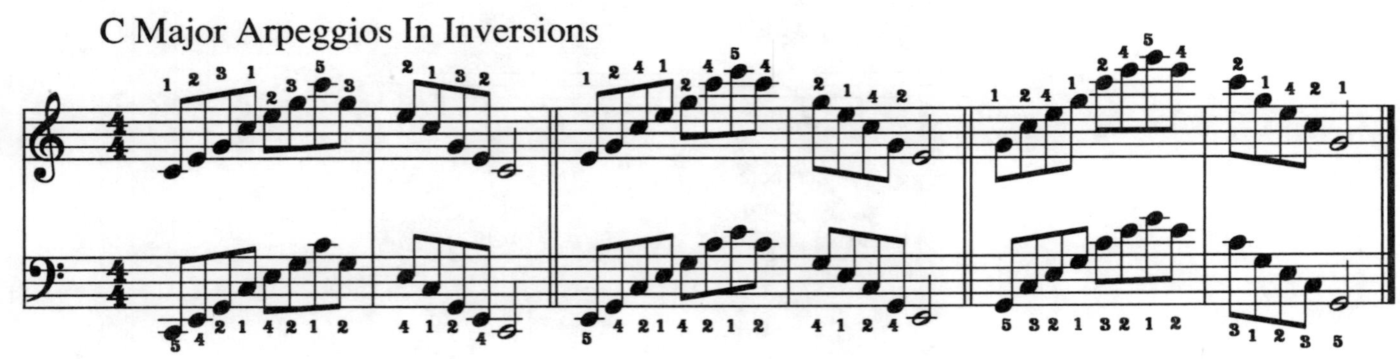

Inversions of Principal Chords of C Major

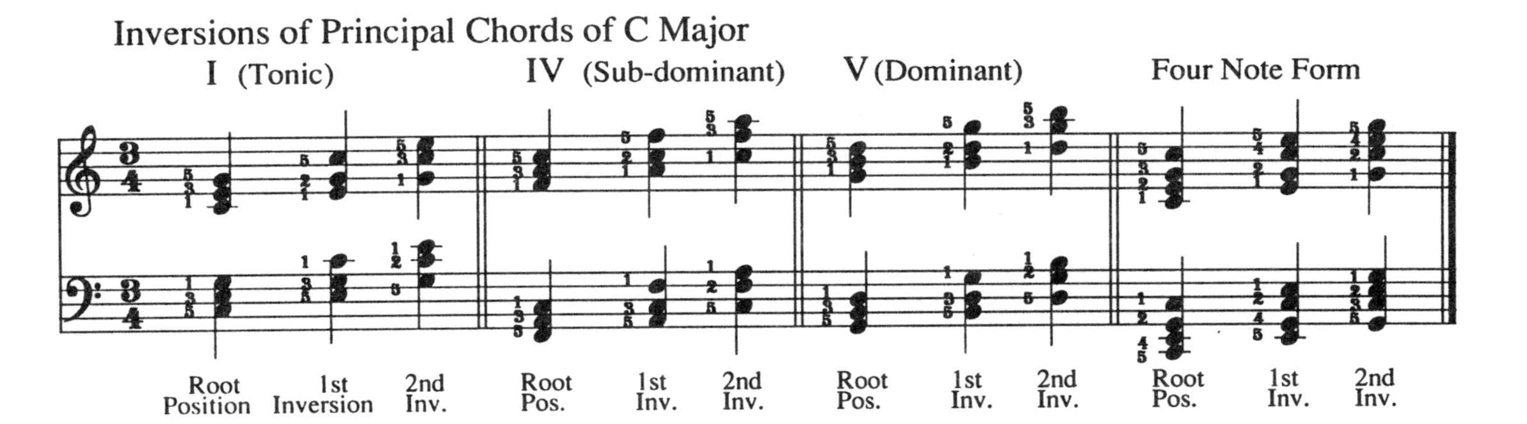
I (Tonic)
IV (Sub-dominant)
V (Dominant)
Four Note Form
Root Position
1st Inversion
2nd Inv.
Root Pos.
1st Inv.
2nd Inv.
Root Pos.
1st Inv.
2nd Inv.
Root Pos.
1st Inv.
2nd Inv.

Cadences In C Major

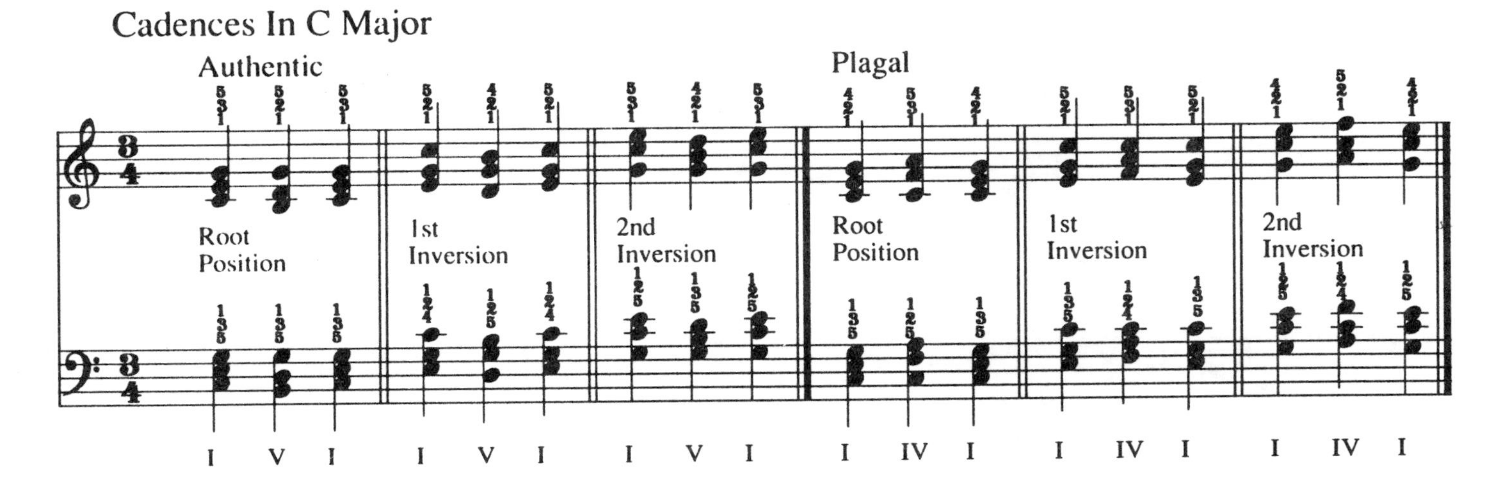
Authentic
Plagal
Root Position
1st Inversion
2nd Inversion
Root Position
1st Inversion
2nd Inversion
I V I
I V I
I V I
I IV I
I IV I
I IV I

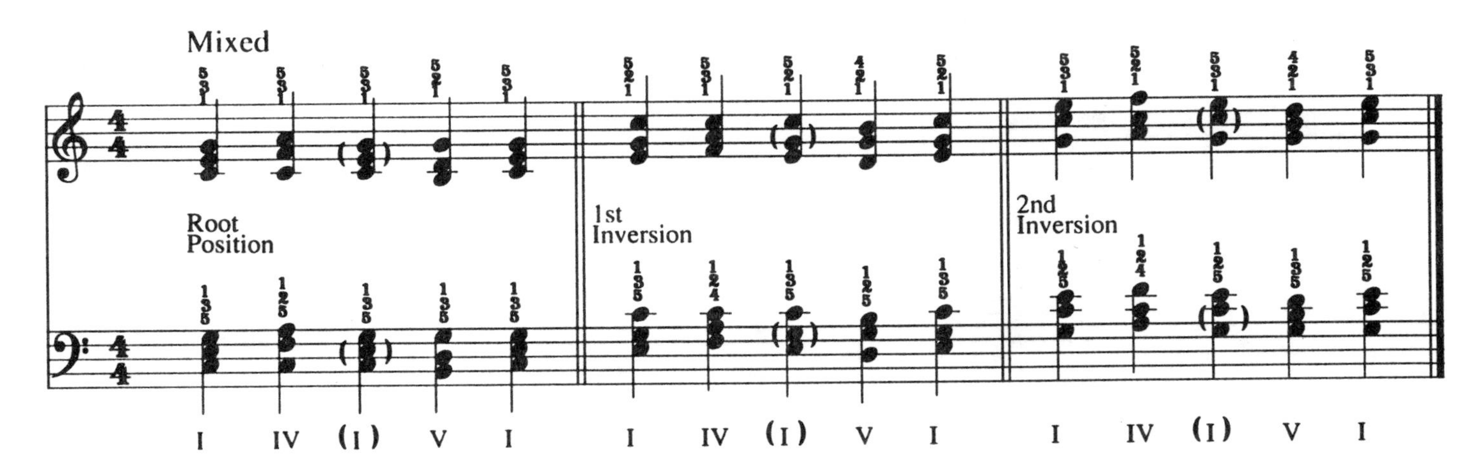
Mixed
Root Position
1st Inversion
2nd Inversion
I IV (I) V I
I IV (I) V I
I IV (I) V I

Key of C (Major or Minor) Dominant Seventh Chords, Arpeggio and Cadence

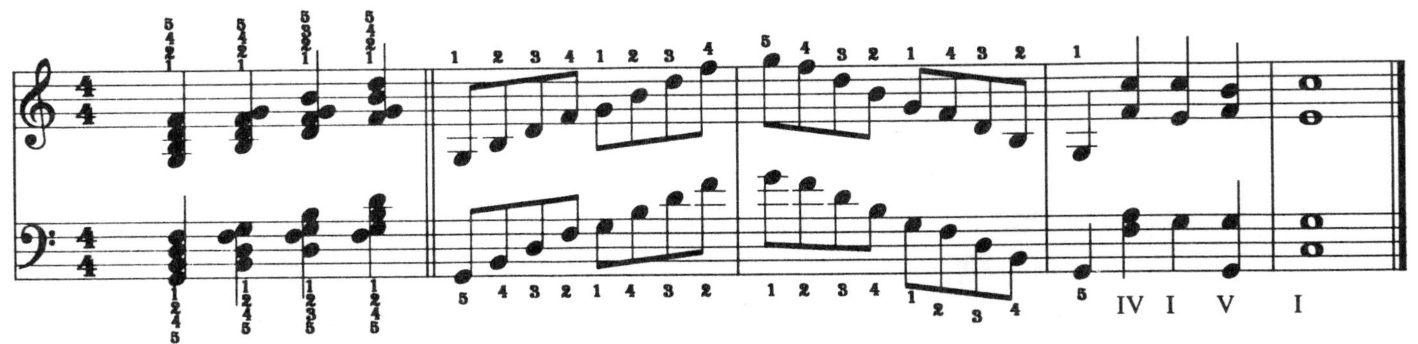
IV I V I

G Major

G Major Scale (1 Octave)

G Major Scale (2 Octaves)

G Major Arpeggio (1 Octave) G Major Arpeggio (2 Octaves)

G Major Arpeggios In Inversions

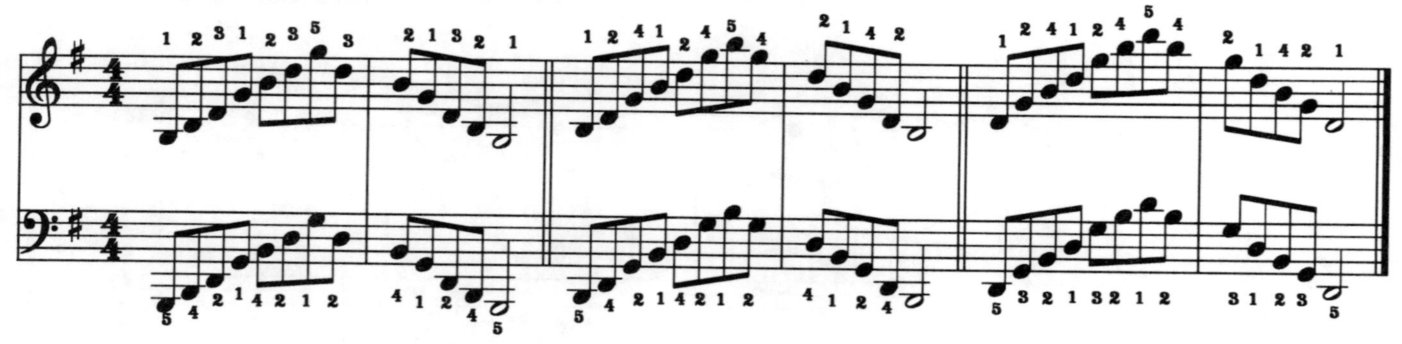

Inversions of Principal Chords of G Major

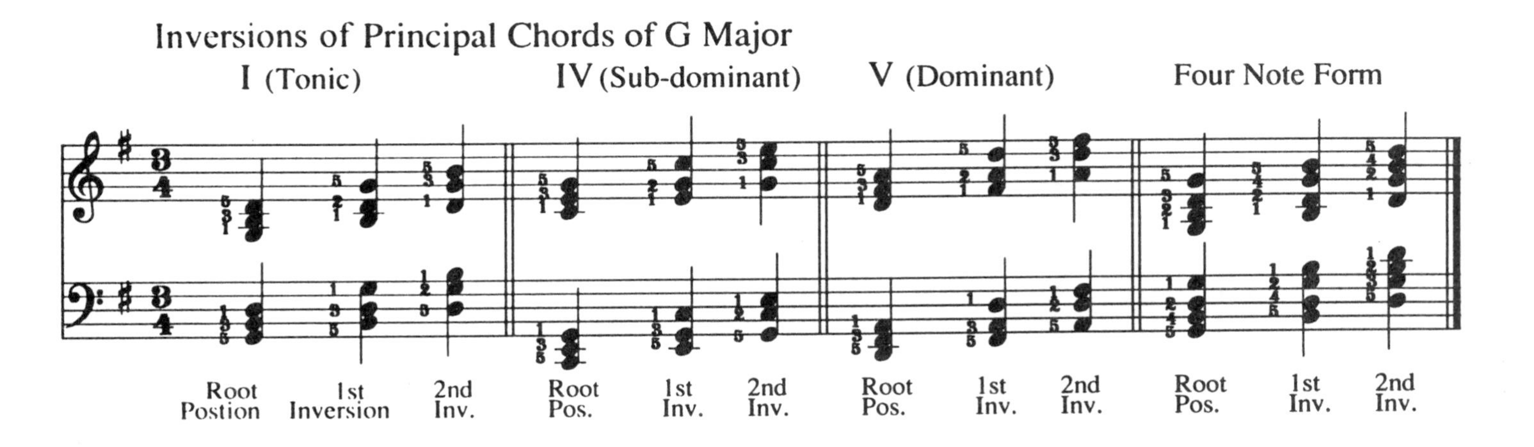
I (Tonic)
IV (Sub-dominant)
V (Dominant)
Four Note Form
Root Postion
1st Inversion
2nd Inv.
Root Pos.
1st Inv.
2nd Inv.
Root Pos.
1st Inv.
2nd Inv.
Root Pos.
1st Inv.
2nd Inv.

Cadences In G Major

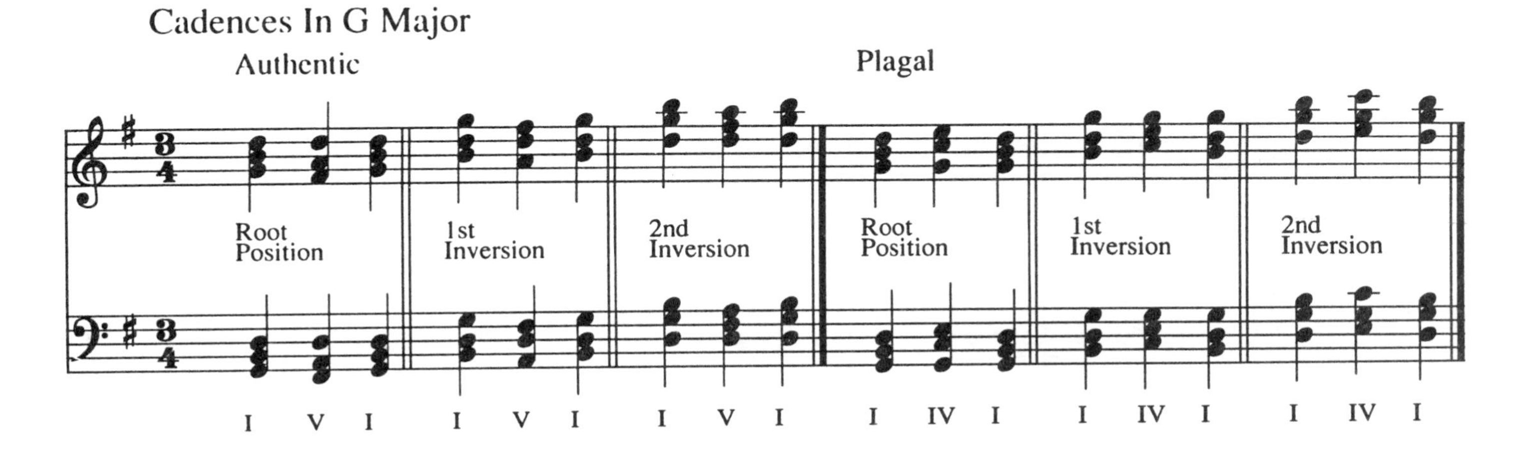
Authentic
Plagal
Root Position
1st Inversion
2nd Inversion
Root Position
1st Inversion
2nd Inversion
I V I
I V I
I V I
I IV I
I IV I
I IV I

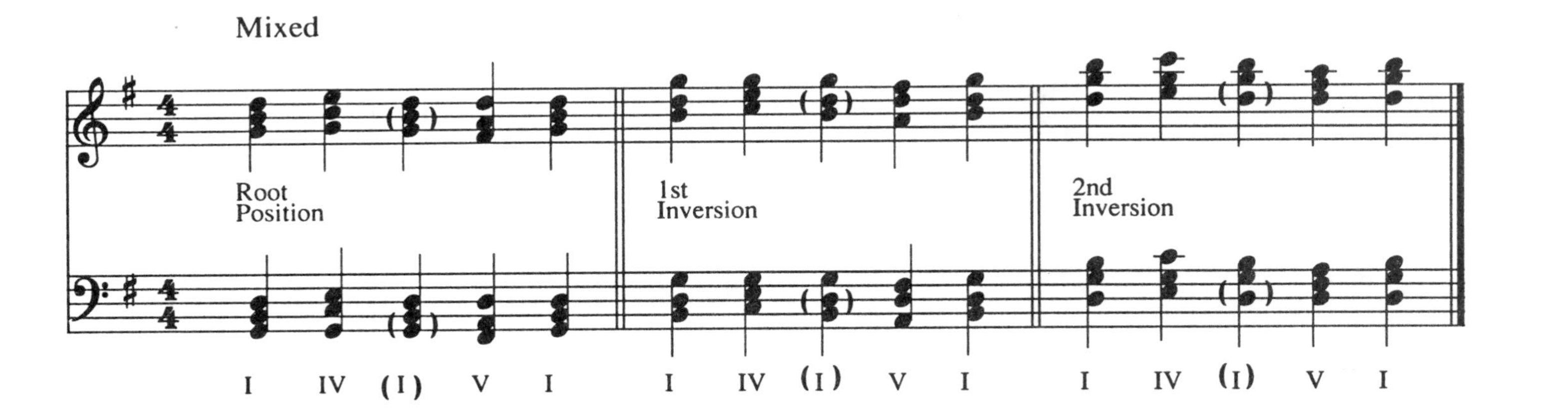
Mixed
Root Position
1st Inversion
2nd Inversion
I IV (I) V I
I IV (I) V I
I IV (I) V I

Key of G (Major or Minor) Dominant Seventh Chords, Arpeggio and Cadence

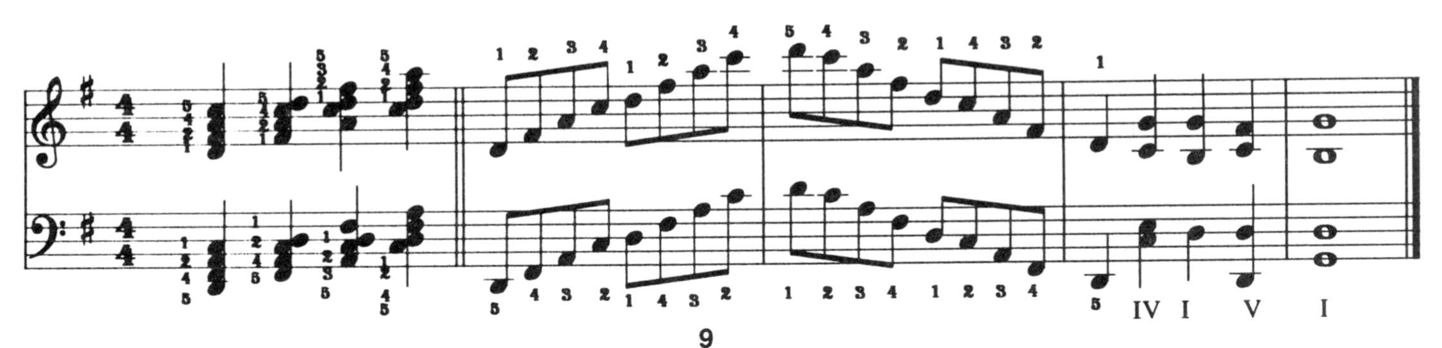
IV I V I

D Major

D Major Scale (1 Octave)

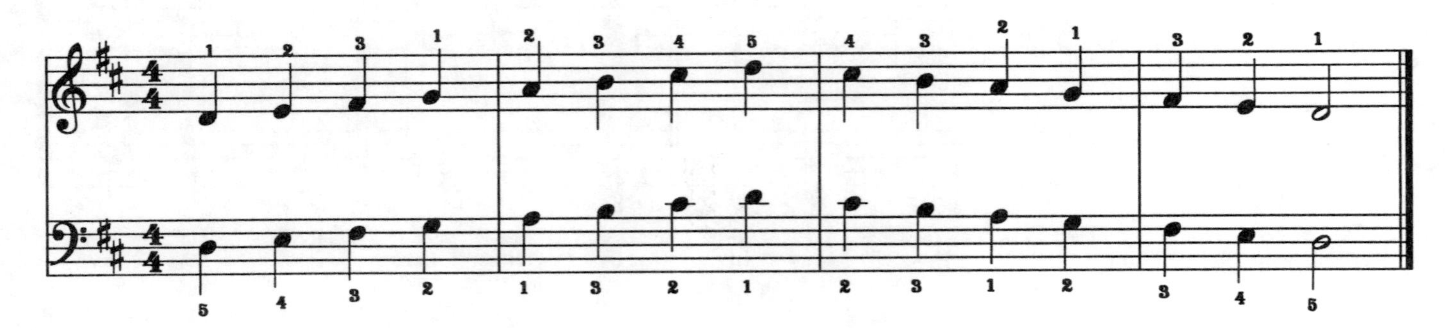

D Major Scale (2 Octaves)

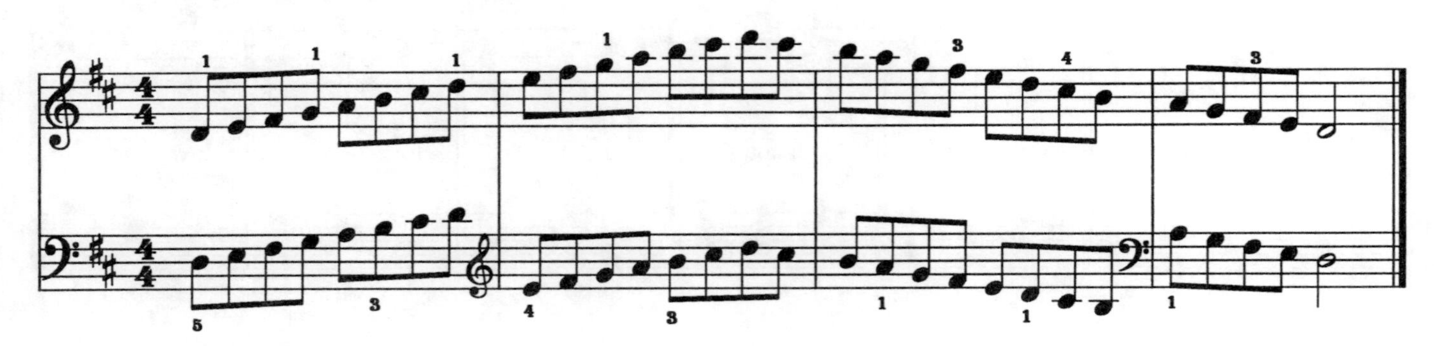

D Major Arpeggio (1 Octave) D Major Arpeggio (2 Octaves)

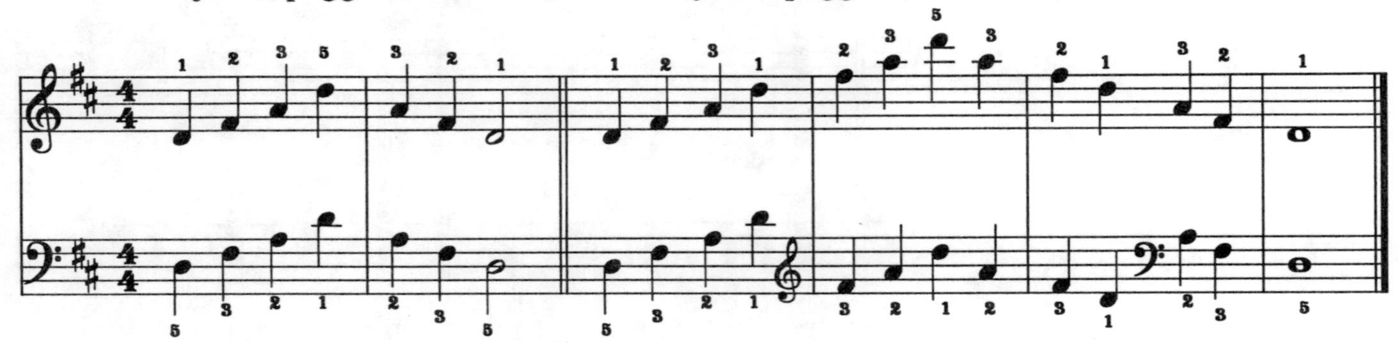

D Major Arpeggios In Inversions

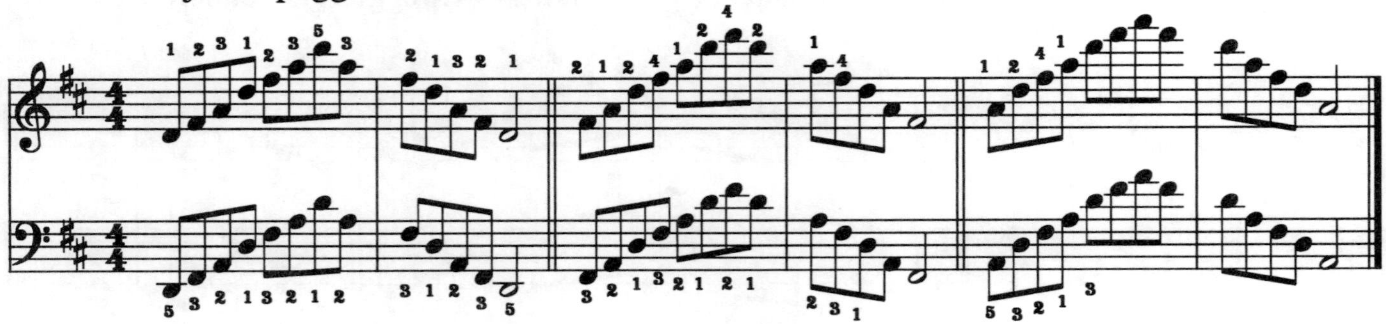

Inversions of Principal Chords of D Major

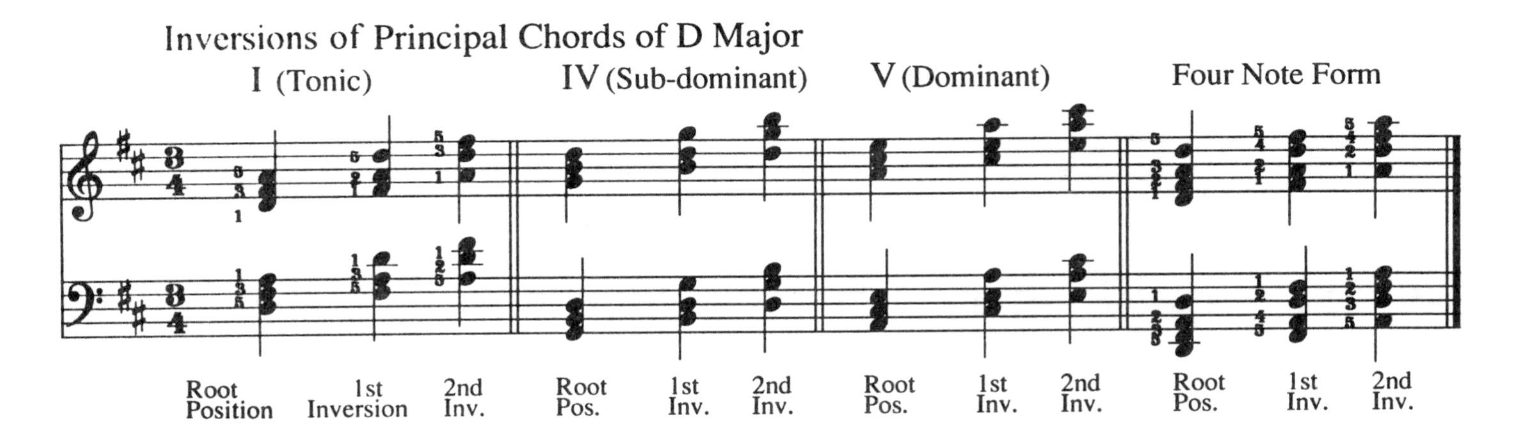
I (Tonic)
IV (Sub-dominant)
V (Dominant)
Four Note Form
Root Position
1st Inversion
2nd Inv.
Root Pos.
1st Inv.
2nd Inv.
Root Pos.
1st Inv.
2nd Inv.
Root Pos.
1st Inv.
2nd Inv.

Cadences In D Major

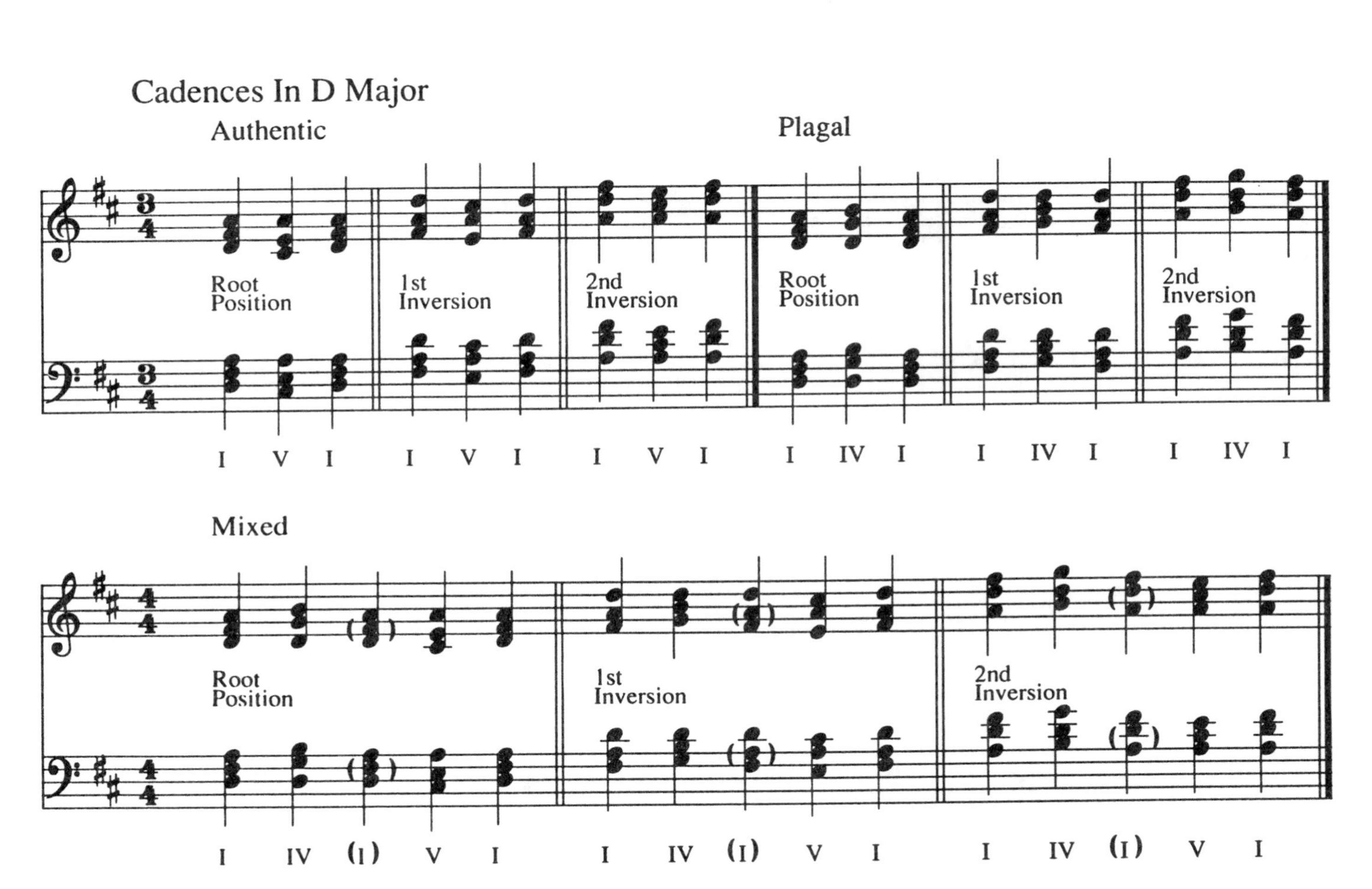
Authentic
Plagal
Root Position
1st Inversion
2nd Inversion
Root Position
1st Inversion
2nd Inversion
I V I
I V I
I V I
I IV I
I IV I
I IV I
Mixed
Root Position
1st Inversion
2nd Inversion
I IV (I) V I
I IV (I) V I
I IV (I) V I

Key of D (Major or Minor) Dominant Seventh Chords, Arpeggio and Cadence

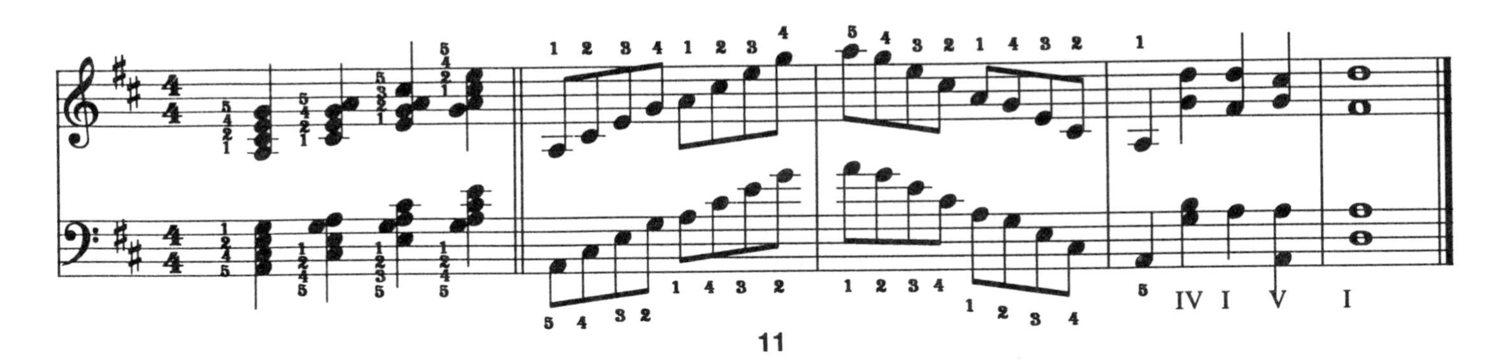
IV I V I

A Major

A Major Scale (1 Octave)

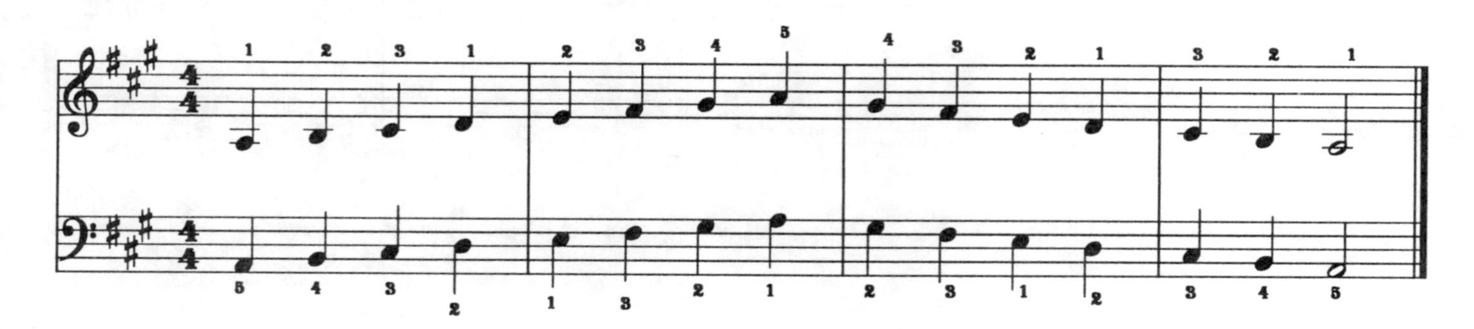

A Major Scale (2 Octaves)

A Major Arpeggio (1 Octave) A Major Arpeggio (2 Octaves)

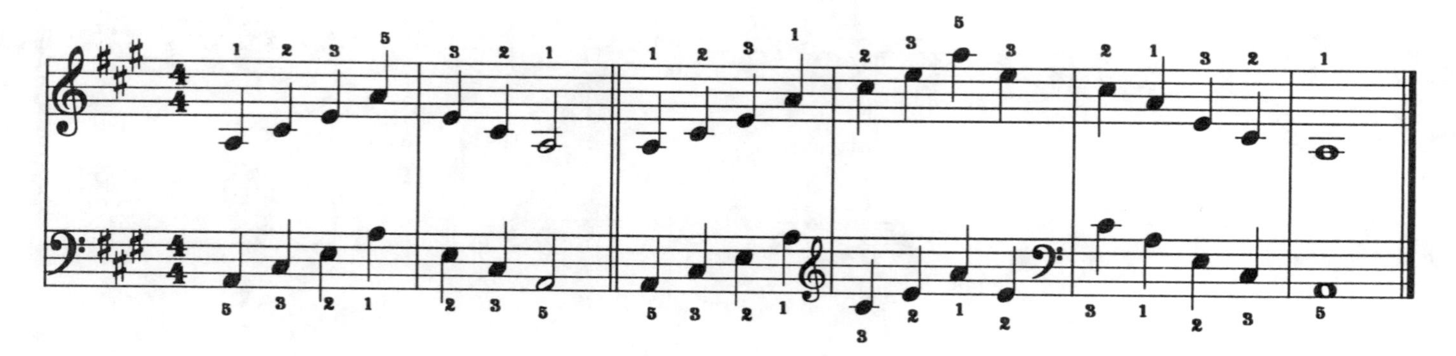

A Major Arpeggios In Inversions

Inversions of Principal Chords of A Major

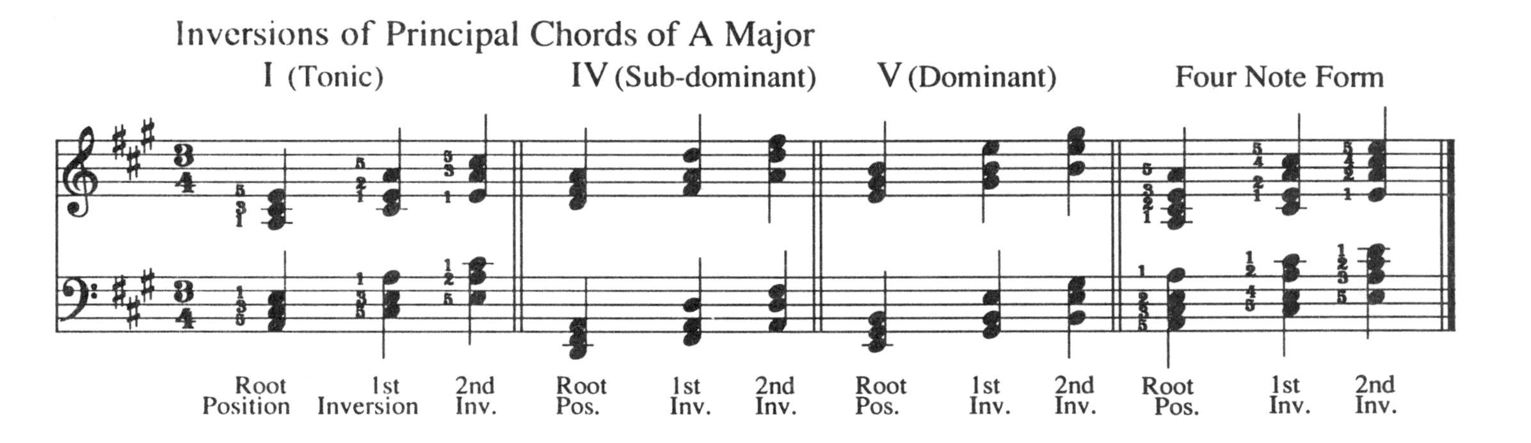
I (Tonic)
IV (Sub-dominant)
V (Dominant)
Four Note Form
Root Position
1st Inversion
2nd Inv.
Root Pos.
1st Inv.
2nd Inv.
Root Pos.
1st Inv.
2nd Inv.
Root Pos.
1st Inv.
2nd Inv.

Cadences In A Major

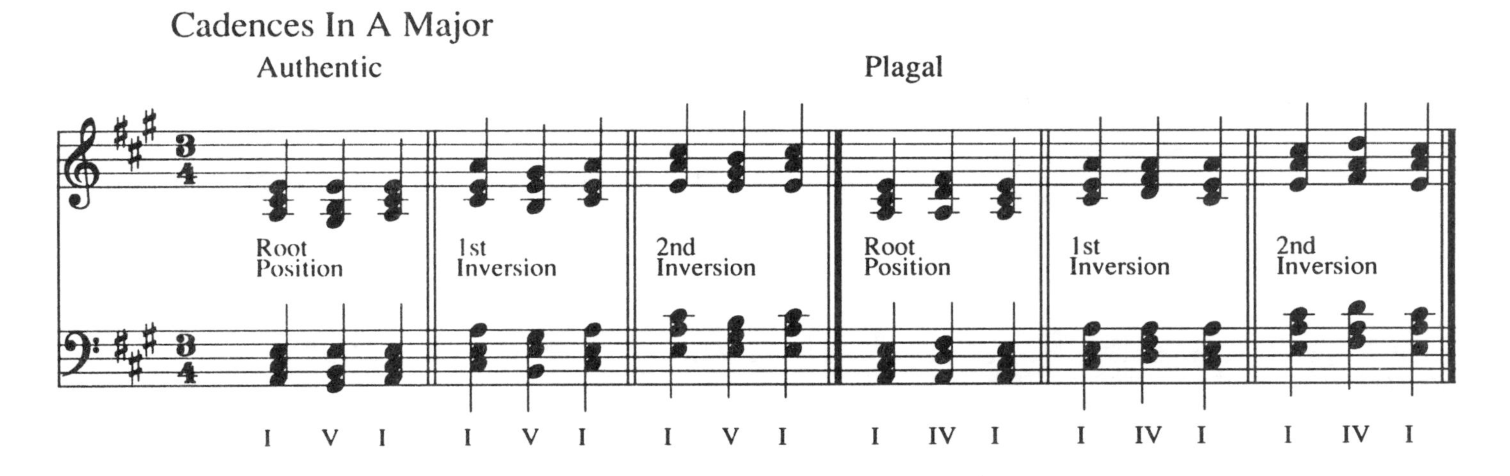
Authentic
Plagal
Root Position
1st Inversion
2nd Inversion
Root Position
1st Inversion
2nd Inversion
I V I
I V I
I V I
I IV I
I IV I
I IV I

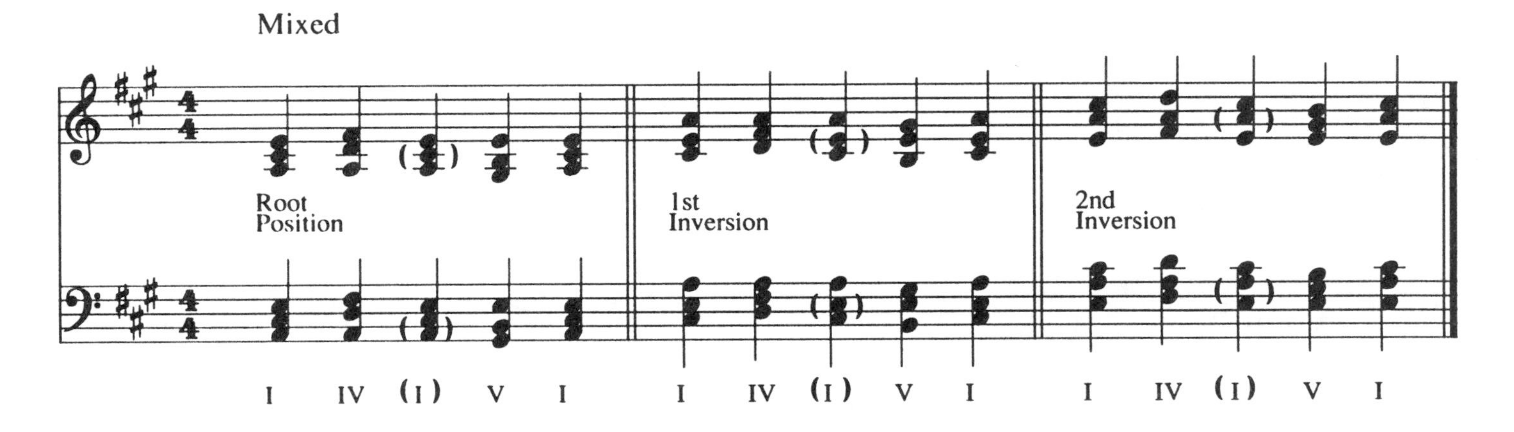
Mixed
Root Position
1st Inversion
2nd Inversion
I IV (I) V I
I IV (I) V I
I IV (I) V I

Key of A (Major or Minor) Dominant Seventh Chords, Arpeggio and Cadence

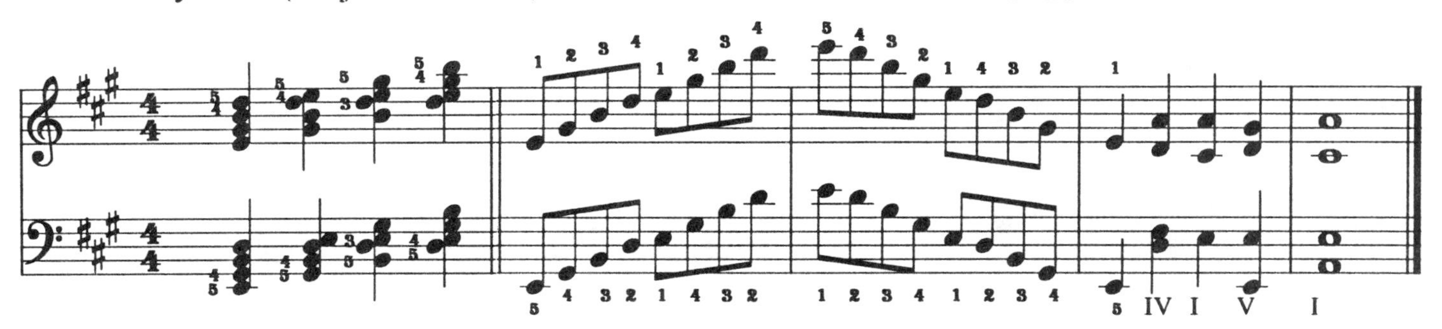
IV I V I

E Major

E Major Scale (1 Octave)

E Major Scale (2 Octaves)

E Major Arpeggio (1 Octave)   E Major Arpeggio (2 Octaves)

E Major Arpeggios In Inversions

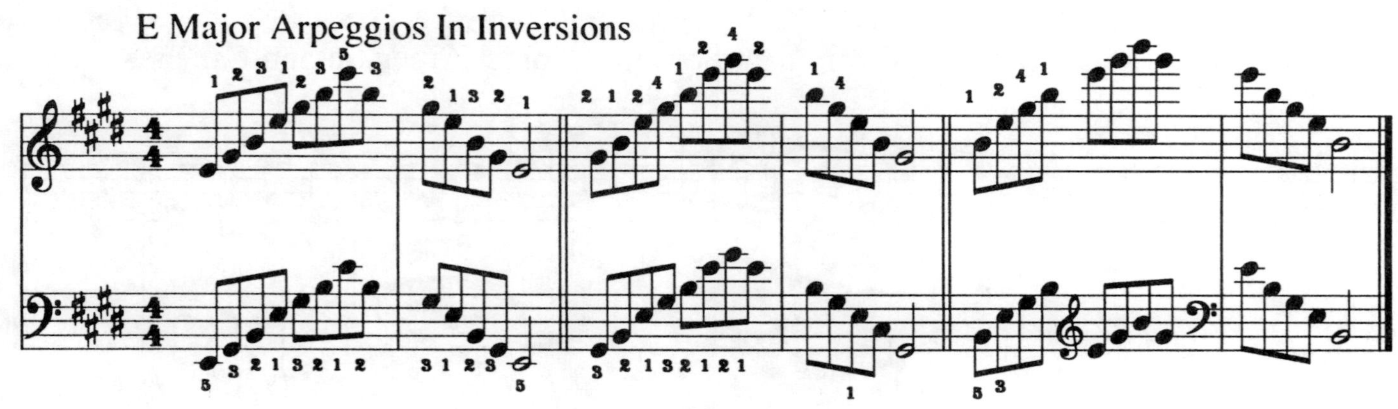

Inversions of Principal Chords of E Major

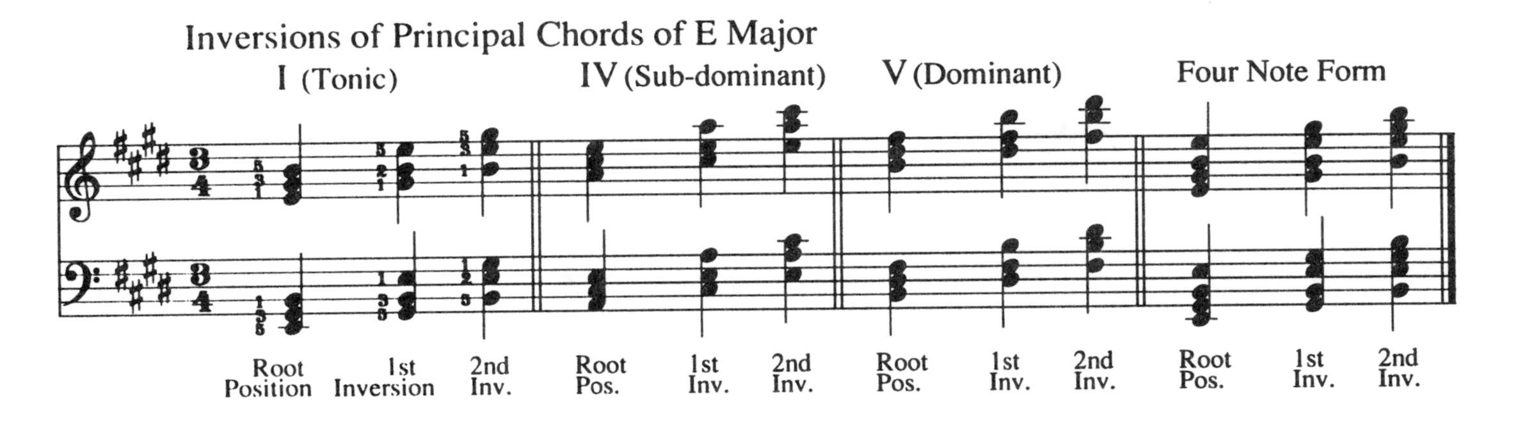
I (Tonic)
IV (Sub-dominant)
V (Dominant)
Four Note Form
Root Position
1st Inversion
2nd Inv.
Root Pos.
1st Inv.
2nd Inv.
Root Pos.
1st Inv.
2nd Inv.
Root Pos.
1st Inv.
2nd Inv.

Cadences In E Major

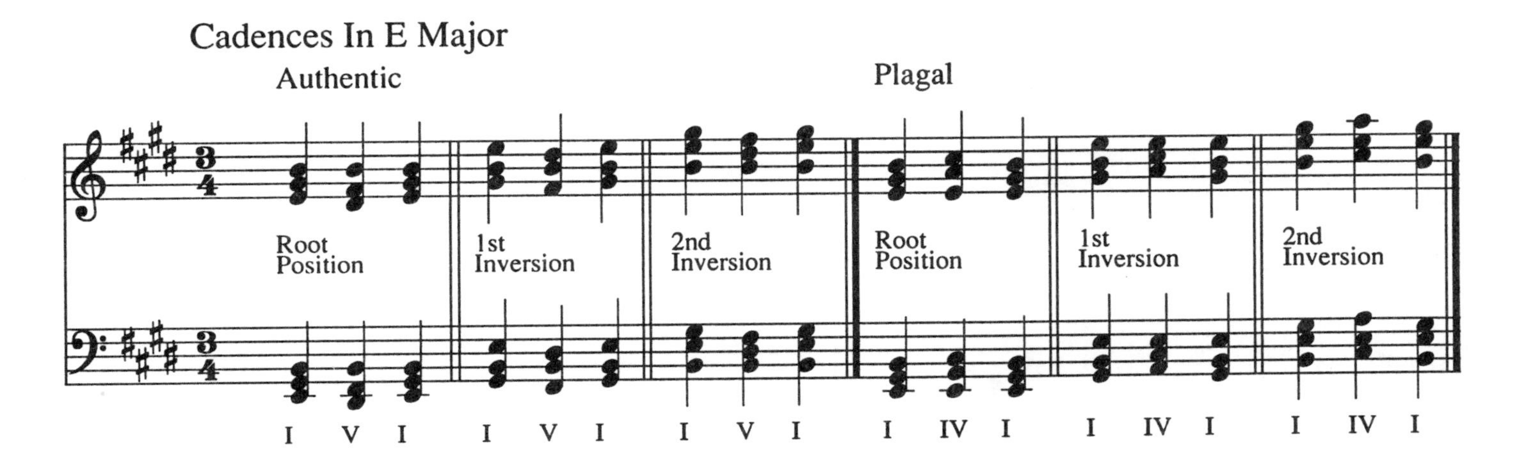
Authentic
Plagal
Root Position
1st Inversion
2nd Inversion
Root Position
1st Inversion
2nd Inversion
I V I
I V I
I V I
I IV I
I IV I
I IV I

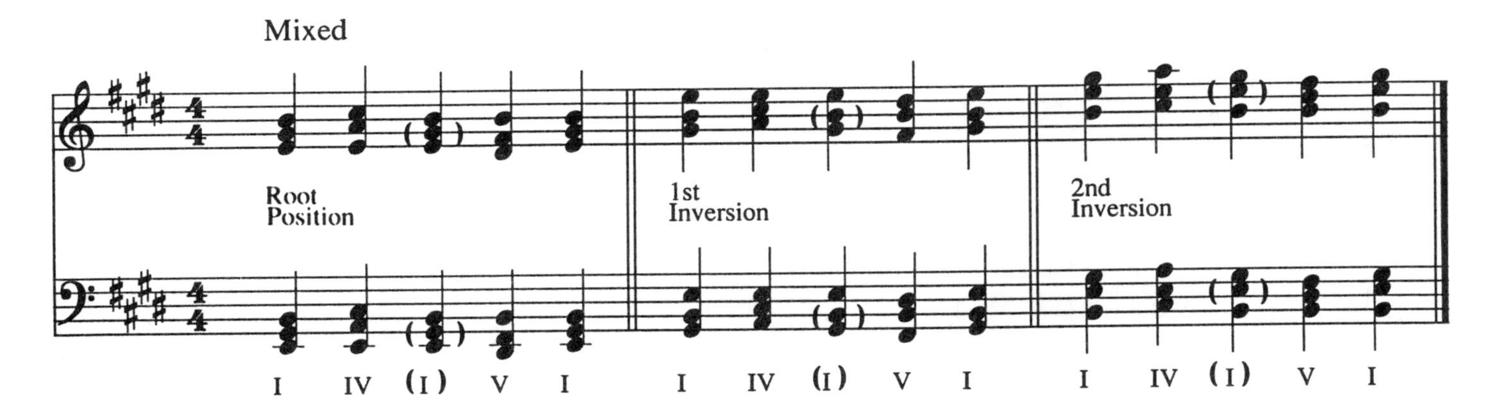
Mixed
Root Position
1st Inversion
2nd Inversion
I IV (I) V I
I IV (I) V I
I IV (I) V I

Key of E (Major or Minor) Dominant Seventh Chords, Arpeggio and Cadence

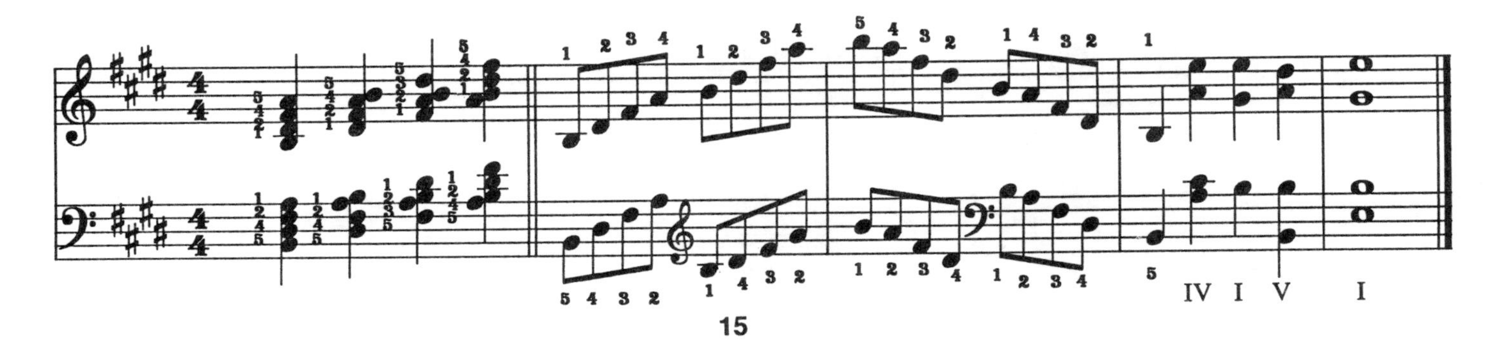
IV I V I

B Major

B Major Scale (1 Octave)

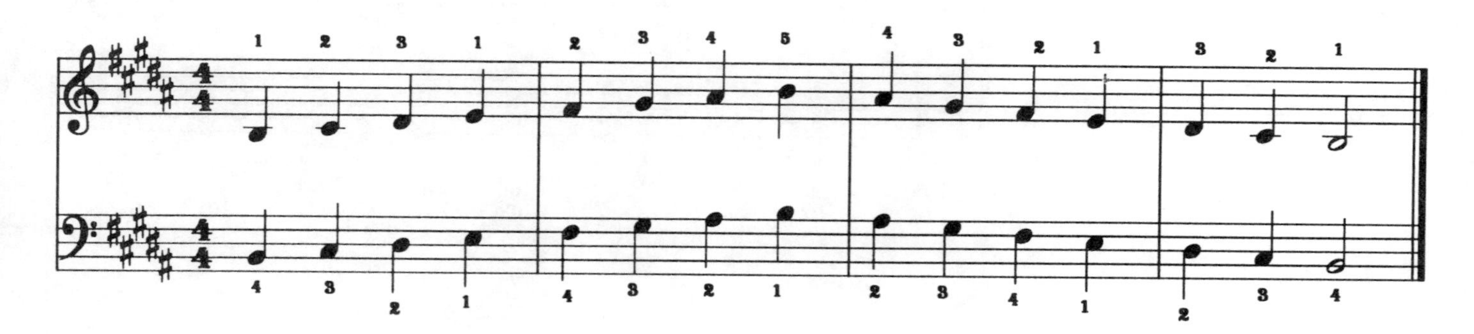

B Major Scale (2 Octaves)

B Major Arpeggio (1 Octave) B Major Arpeggio (2 Octaves)

B Major Arpeggios In Inversions

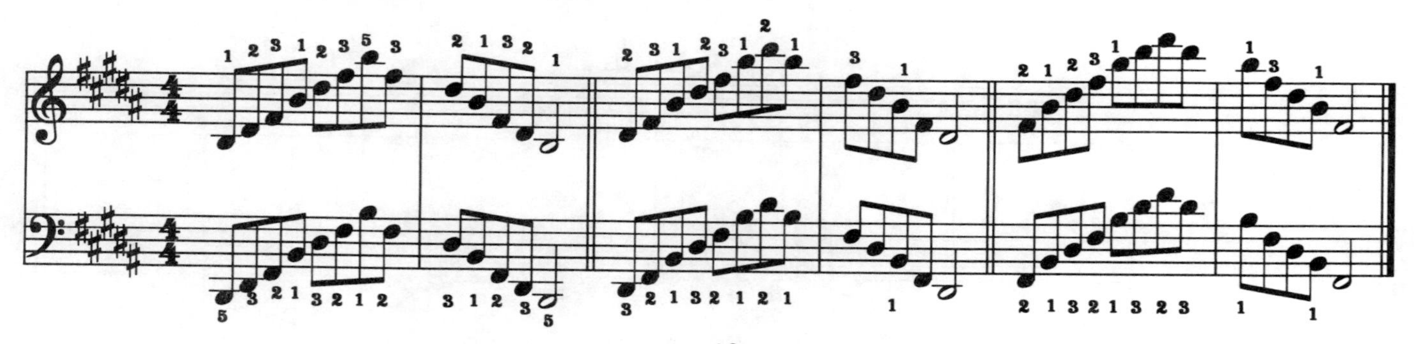

Inversions of Principal Chords of B Major

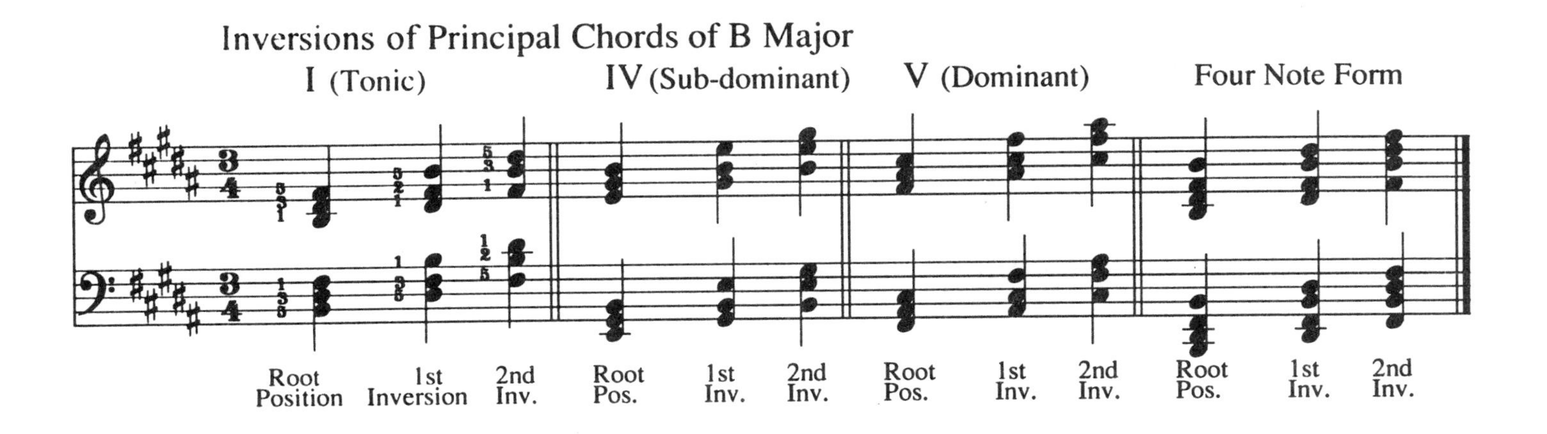
I (Tonic)
IV (Sub-dominant)
V (Dominant)
Four Note Form
Root Position
1st Inversion
2nd Inv.
Root Pos.
1st Inv.
2nd Inv.
Root Pos.
1st Inv.
2nd Inv.
Root Pos.
1st Inv.
2nd Inv.

Cadences In B Major

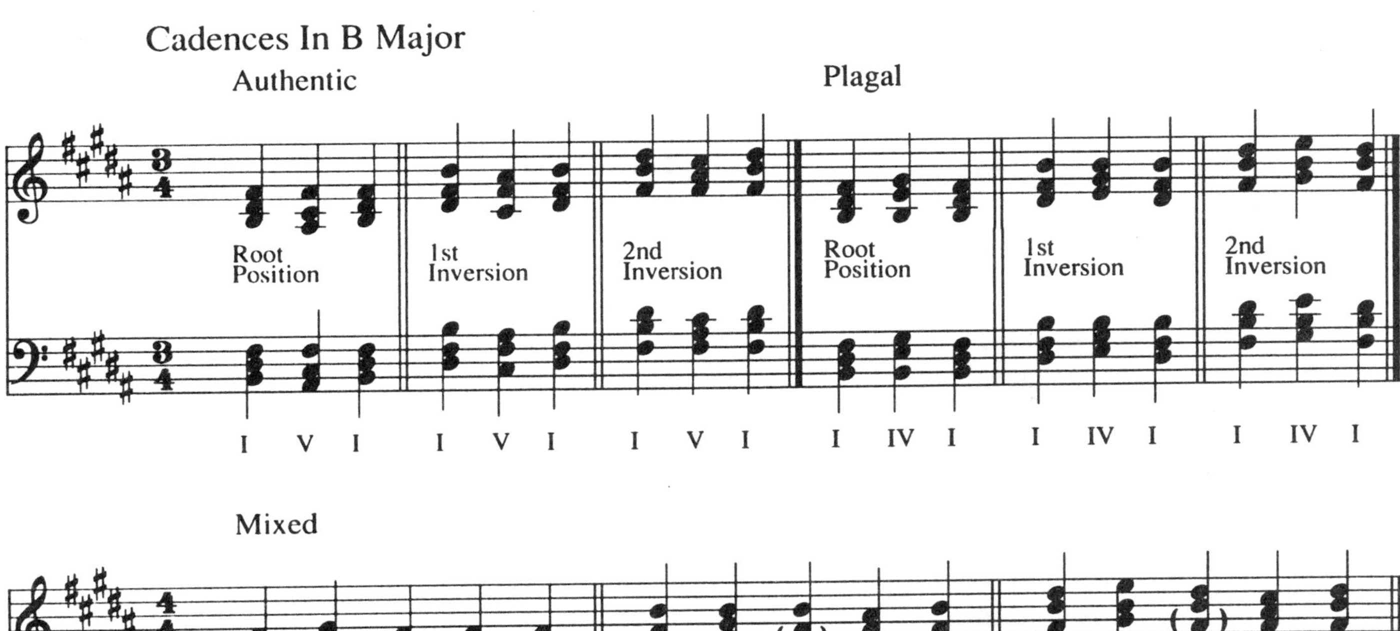
Authentic
Plagal
Root Position
1st Inversion
2nd Inversion
Root Position
1st Inversion
2nd Inversion
I V I
I V I
I V I
I IV I
I IV I
I IV I

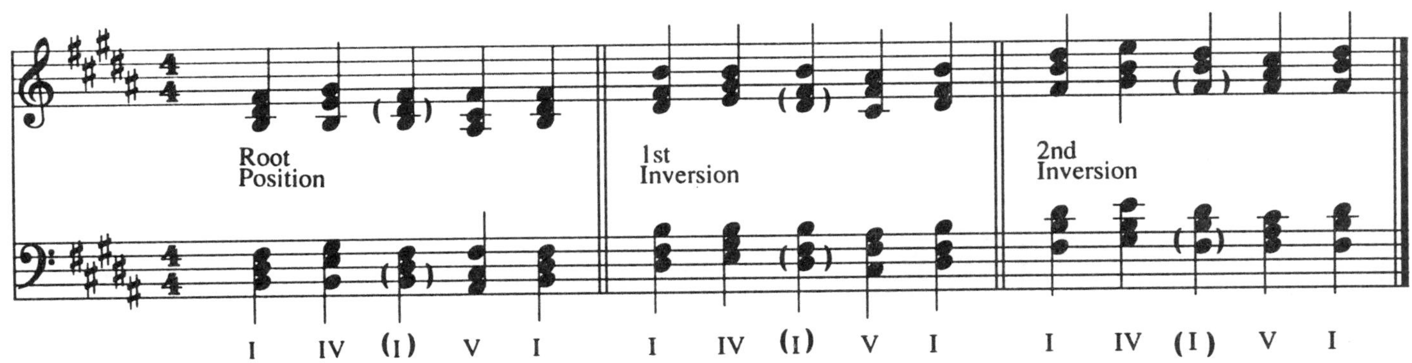
Mixed
Root Position
1st Inversion
2nd Inversion
I IV (I) V I
I IV (I) V I
I IV (I) V I

Key of B (Major or Minor) Dominant Seventh Chords, Arpeggio and Cadence

IV I V I

F Major

F Major Scale (1 Octave)

F Major Scale (2 Octaves)

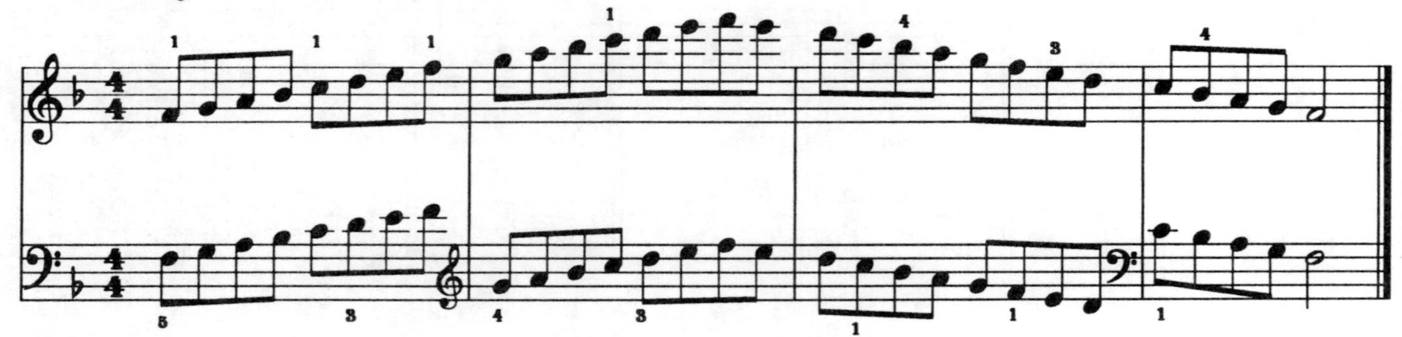

F Major Arpeggio (1 Octave) F Major Arpeggio (2 Octaves)

F Major Arpeggios In Inversions

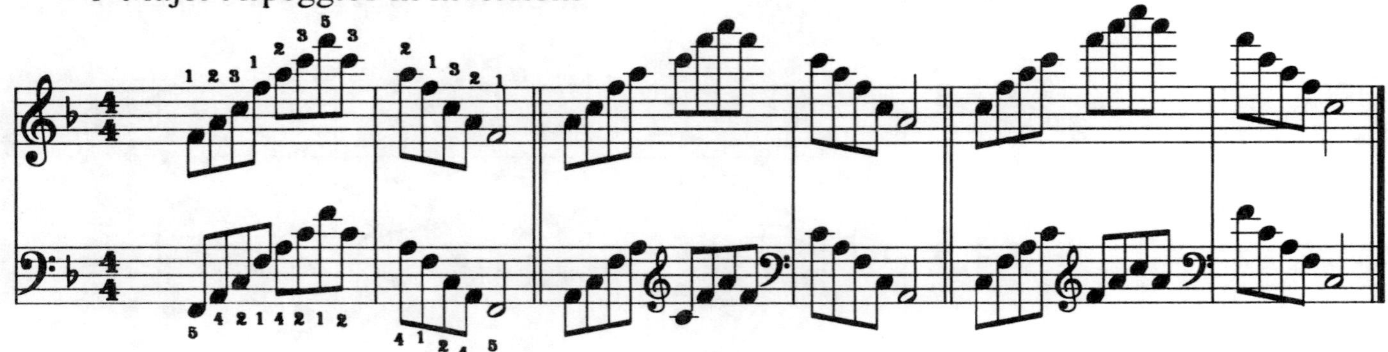

Inversions of Principal Chords of F Major

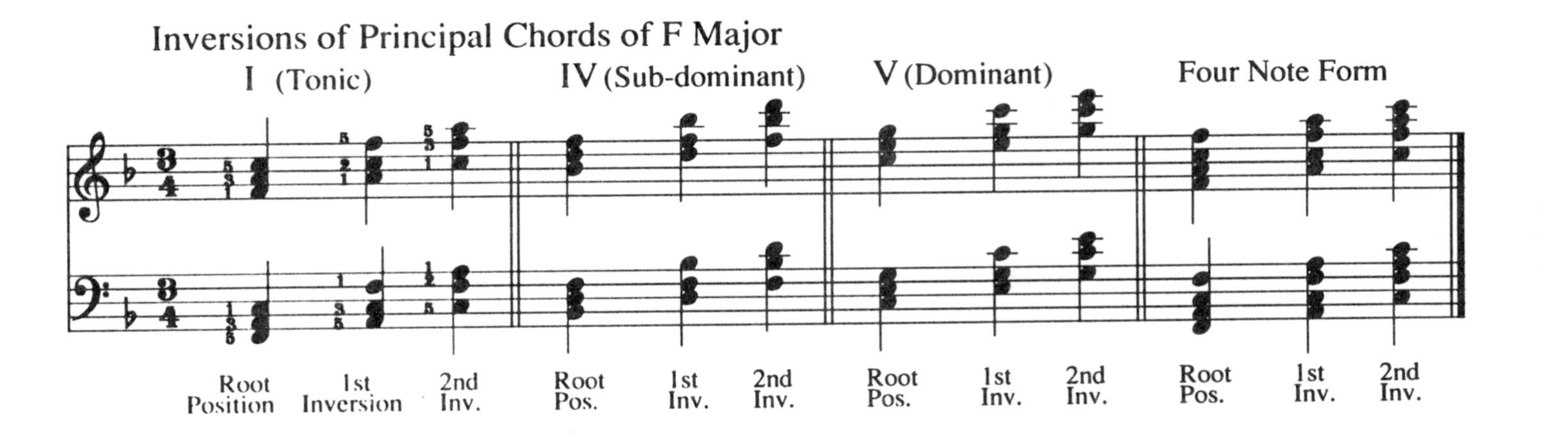
I (Tonic)
IV (Sub-dominant)
V (Dominant)
Four Note Form
Root Position
1st Inversion
2nd Inv.
Root Pos.
1st Inv.
2nd Inv.
Root Pos.
1st Inv.
2nd Inv.
Root Pos.
1st Inv.
2nd Inv.

Cadences In F Major

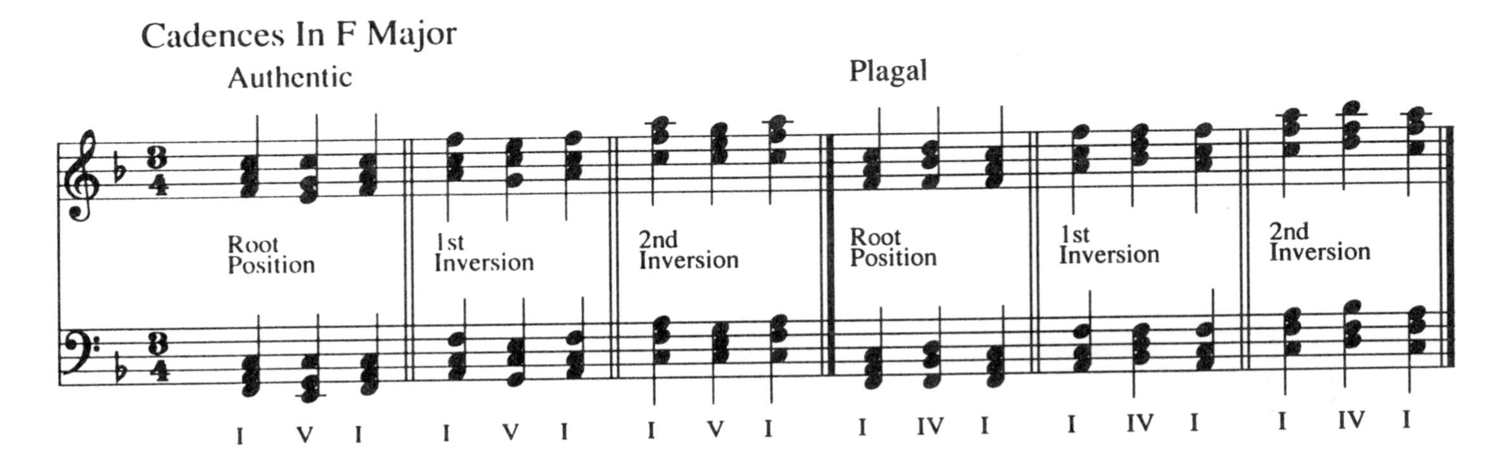
Authentic
Plagal
Root Position
1st Inversion
2nd Inversion
Root Position
1st Inversion
2nd Inversion
I V I
I V I
I V I
I IV I
I IV I
I IV I

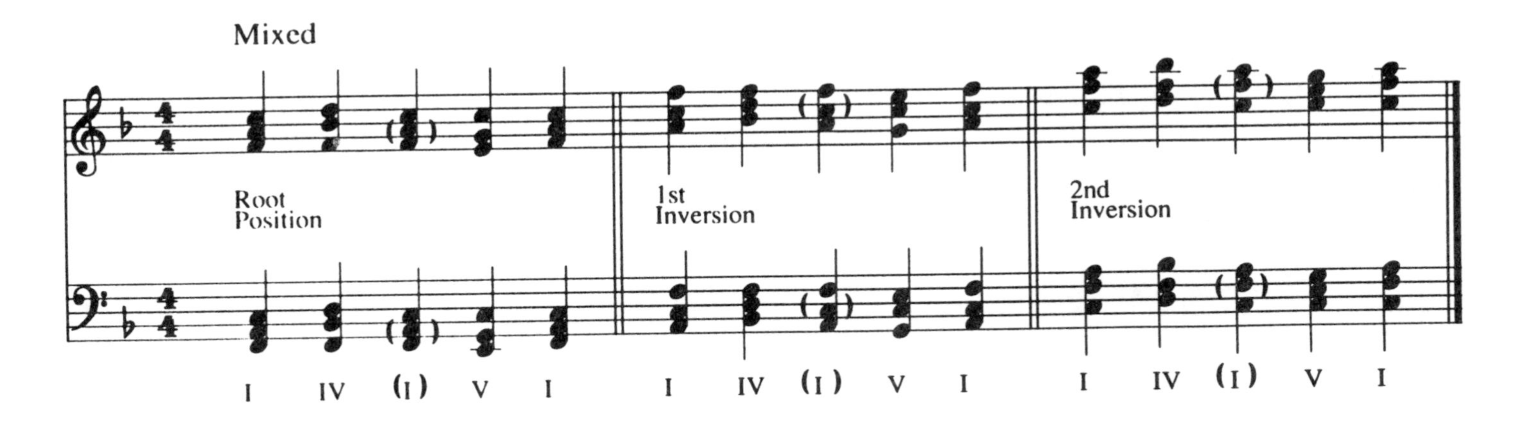
Mixed
Root Position
1st Inversion
2nd Inversion
I IV (I) V I
I IV (I) V I
I IV (I) V I

Key of F (Major or Minor) Dominant Seventh Chords, Arpeggio and Cadence

IV I V I

B Flat Major

B♭ Major Scale (1 Octave)

B♭ Major Scale (2 Octaves)

B♭ Major Arpeggio (1 Octave)   B♭ Major Arpeggio (2 Octaves)

B♭ Major Arpeggios In Inversions

Inversions of Principal Chords of B♭ Major

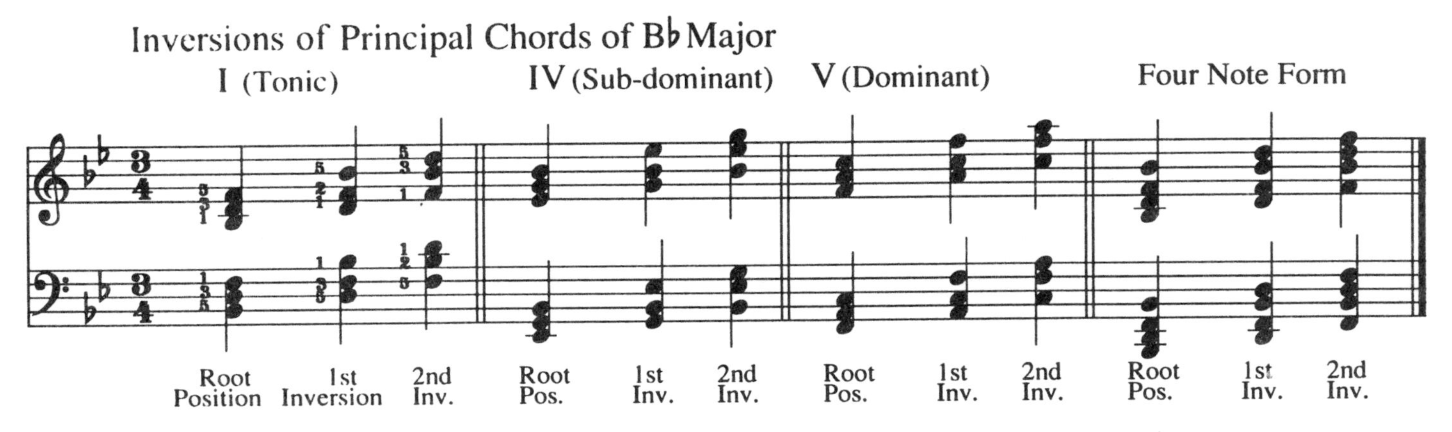
I (Tonic)
IV (Sub-dominant)
V (Dominant)
Four Note Form
Root Position
1st Inversion
2nd Inv.
Root Pos.
1st Inv.
2nd Inv.
Root Pos.
1st Inv.
2nd Inv.
Root Pos.
1st Inv.
2nd Inv.

Cadences In B♭ Major

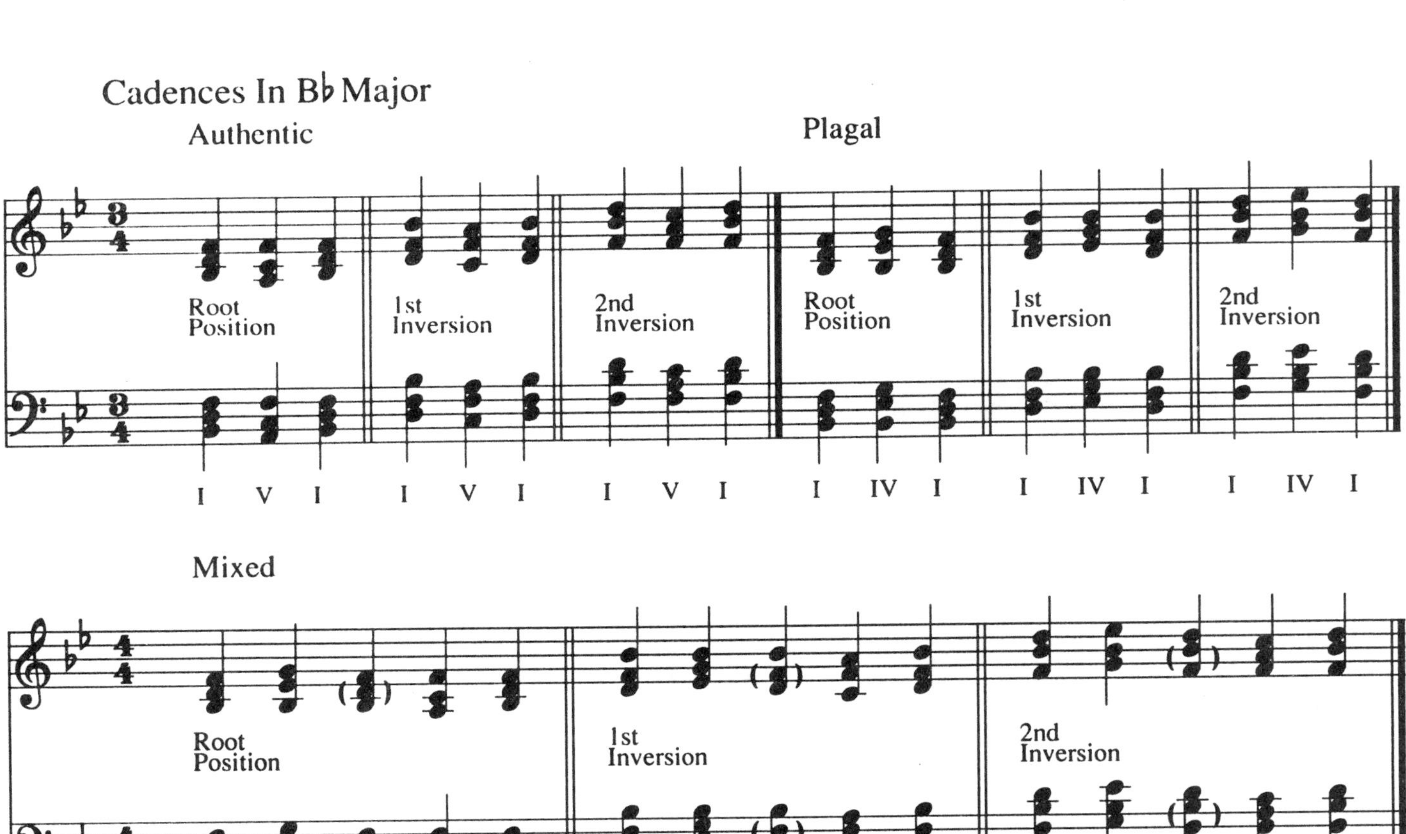
Authentic
Plagal
Root Position
1st Inversion
2nd Inversion
Root Position
1st Inversion
2nd Inversion
I V I
I V I
I V I
I IV I
I IV I
I IV I
Mixed
Root Position
1st Inversion
2nd Inversion
I IV (I) V I
I IV (I) V I
I IV (I) V I

Key of B Flat (Major or Minor) Dominant Seventh Chords, Arpeggio and Cadence

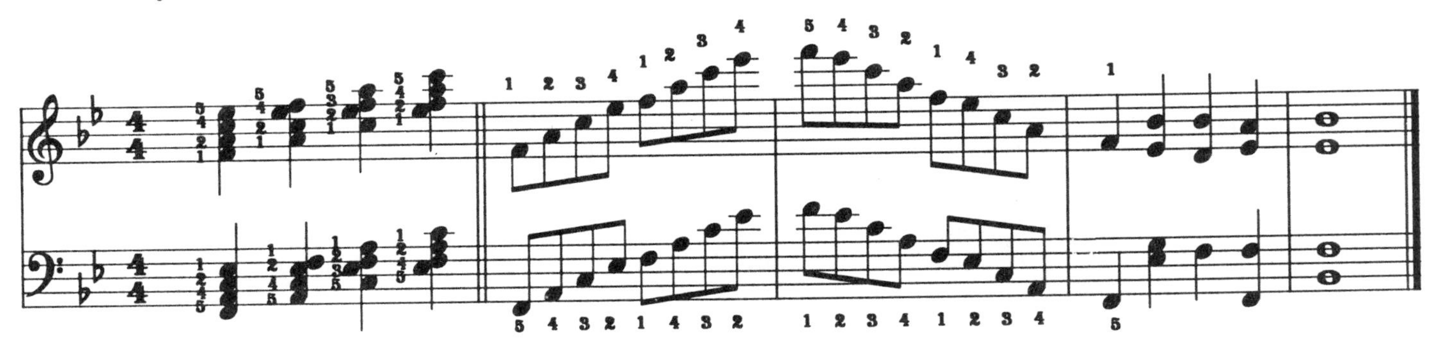

E Flat Major

E♭ Major Scale (1 Octave)

E♭ Major Scale (2 Octaves)

E♭ Major Arpeggio (1 Octave) E♭ Major Arpeggio (2 Octaves)

E♭ Major Arpeggios In Inversions

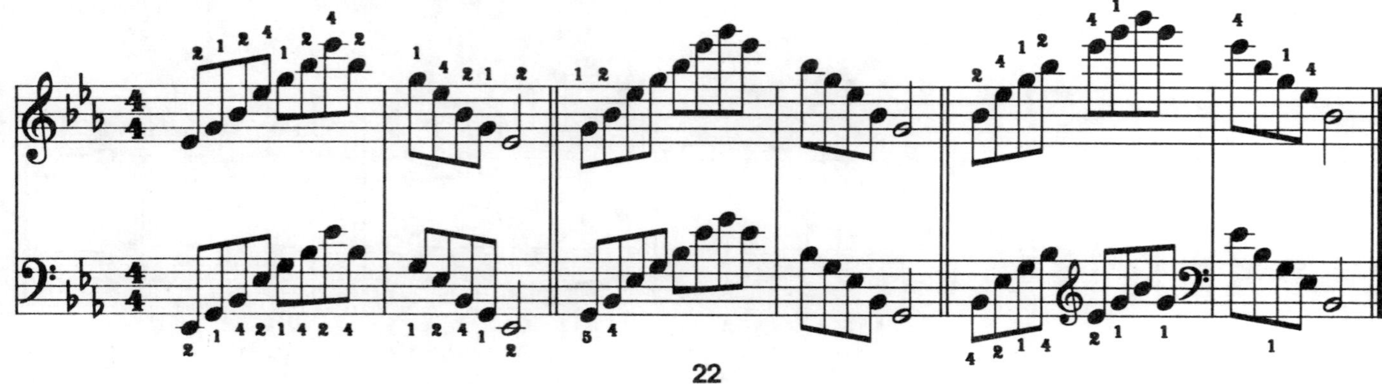

Inversions of Principal Chords of E♭ Major

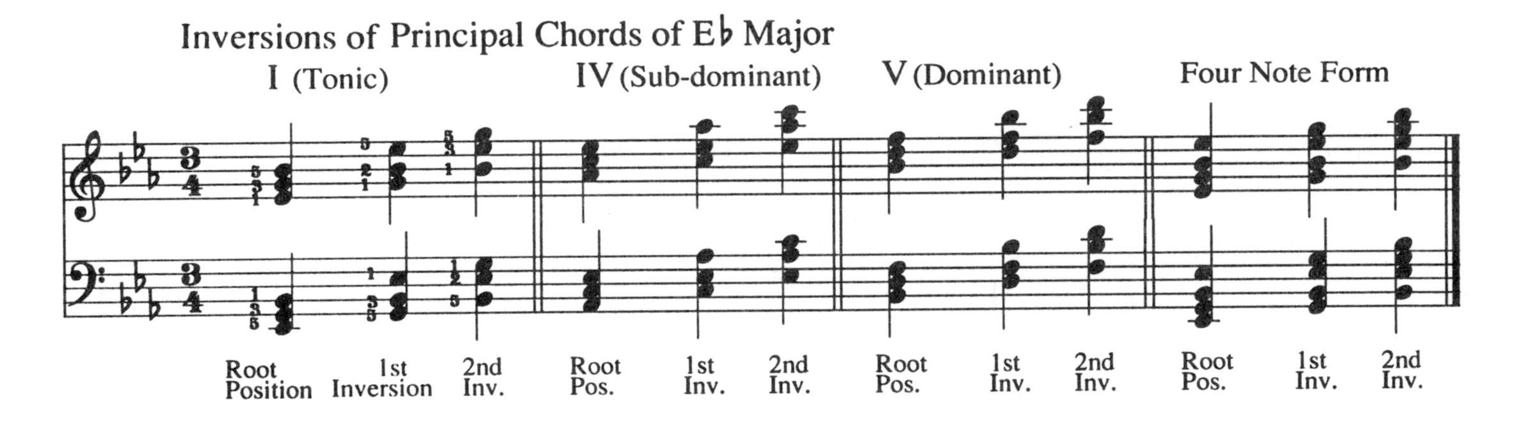
I (Tonic)
IV (Sub-dominant)
V (Dominant)
Four Note Form
Root Position
1st Inversion
2nd Inv.
Root Pos.
1st Inv.
2nd Inv.
Root Pos.
1st Inv.
2nd Inv.
Root Pos.
1st Inv.
2nd Inv.

Cadences In E♭ Major

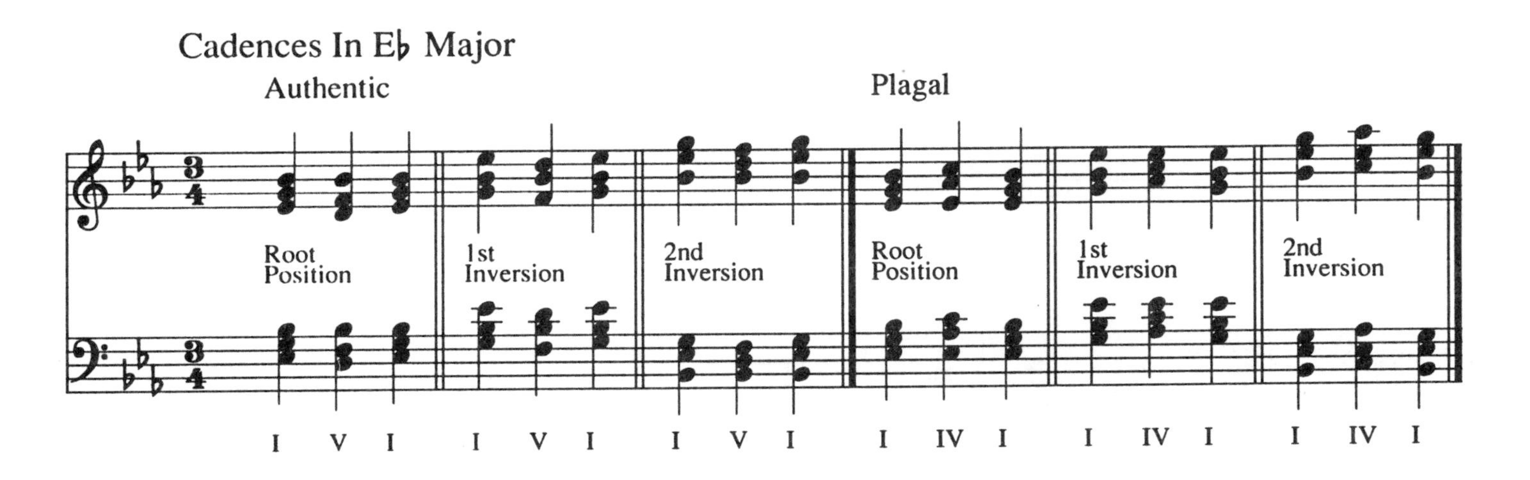
Authentic
Plagal
Root Position
1st Inversion
2nd Inversion
Root Position
1st Inversion
2nd Inversion
I V I
I V I
I V I
I IV I
I IV I
I IV I

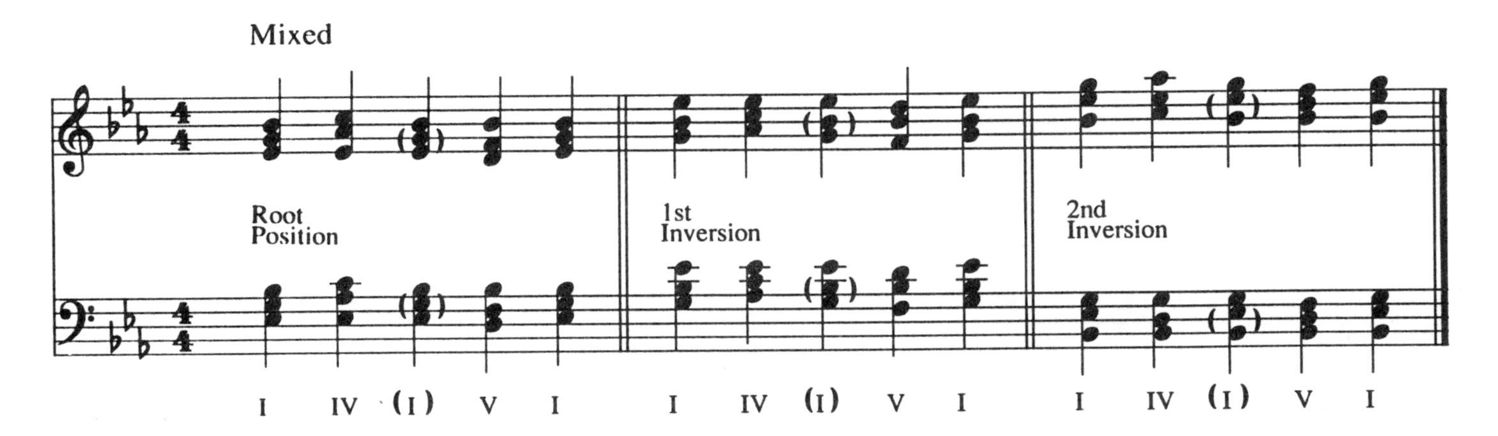
Mixed
Root Position
1st Inversion
2nd Inversion
I IV (I) V I
I IV (I) V I
I IV (I) V I

Key of E Flat (Major or Minor) Dominant Seventh Chords, Arpeggio and Cadence

IV I V I

A Flat Major

A♭ Major Scale (1 Octave)

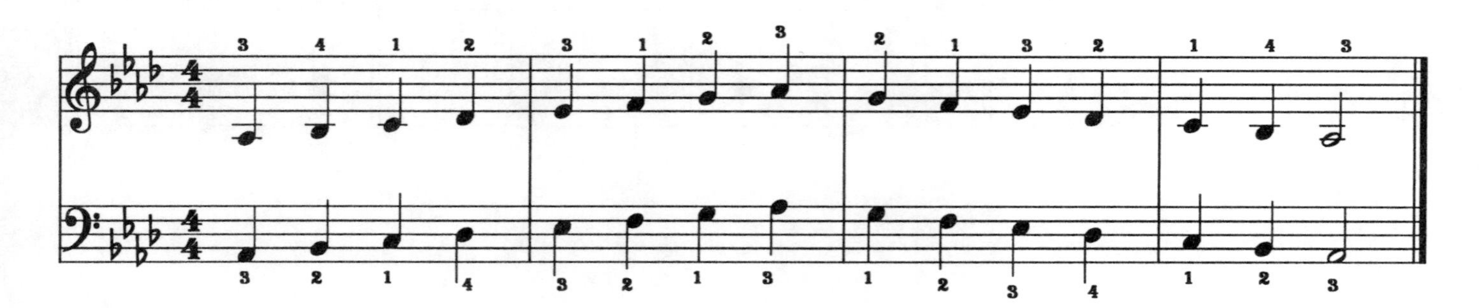

A♭ Major Scale (2 Octaves)

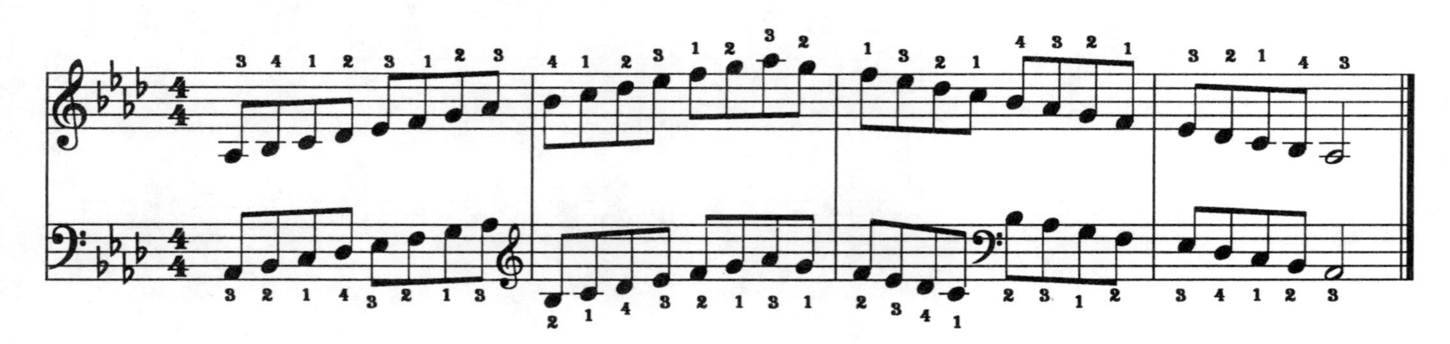

A♭ Major Arpeggio (1 Octave) A♭ Major Arpeggio (2 Octaves)

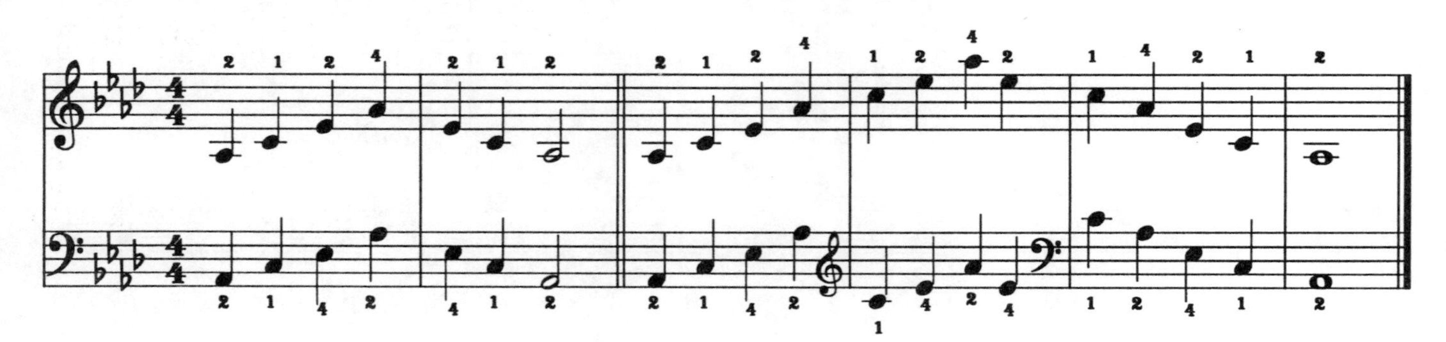

A♭ Major Arpeggios In Inversions

Inversions of Principal Chords of A♭ Major

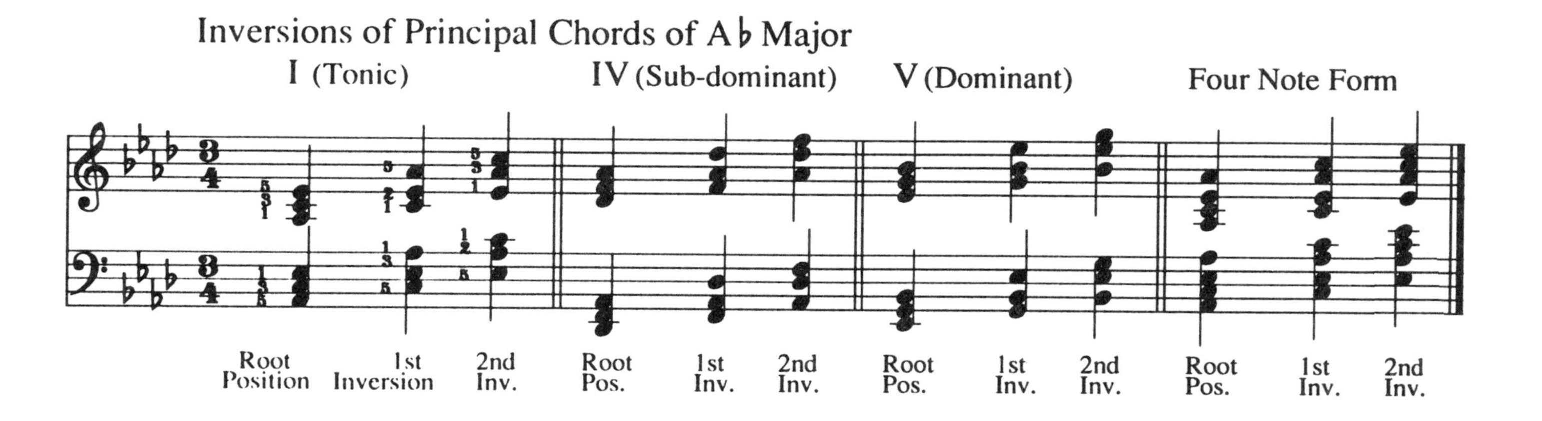
I (Tonic)
IV (Sub-dominant)
V (Dominant)
Four Note Form
Root Position
1st Inversion
2nd Inv.
Root Pos.
1st Inv.
2nd Inv.
Root Pos.
1st Inv.
2nd Inv.
Root Pos.
1st Inv.
2nd Inv.

Cadences In A♭ Major

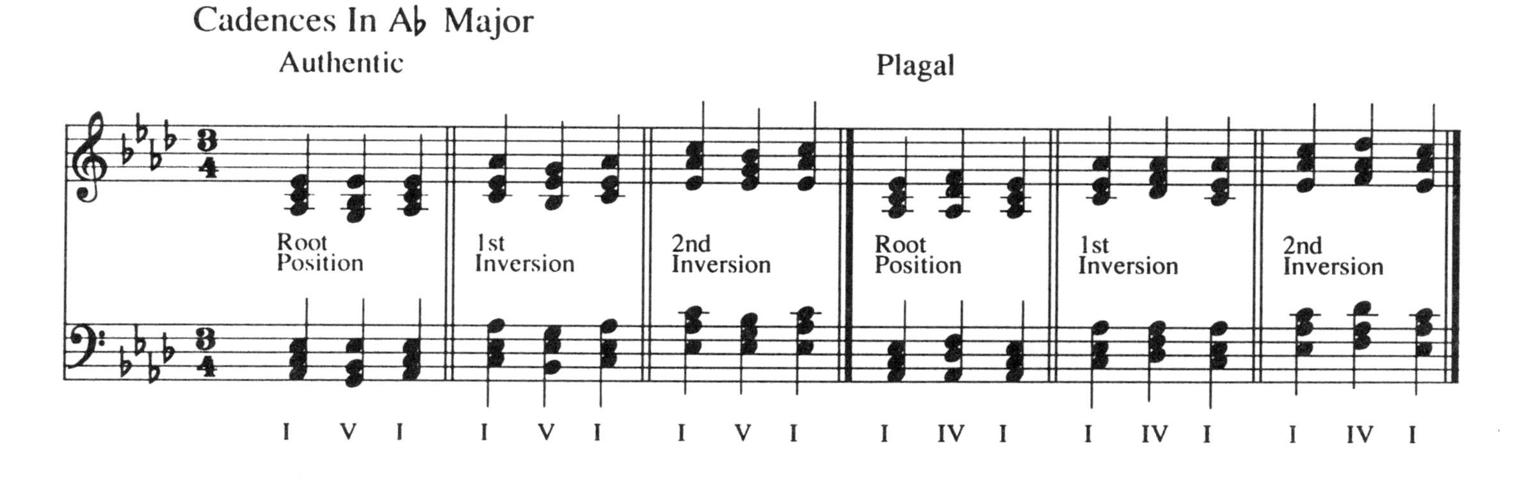
Authentic
Plagal
Root Position
1st Inversion
2nd Inversion
Root Position
1st Inversion
2nd Inversion
I V I
I V I
I V I
I IV I
I IV I
I IV I

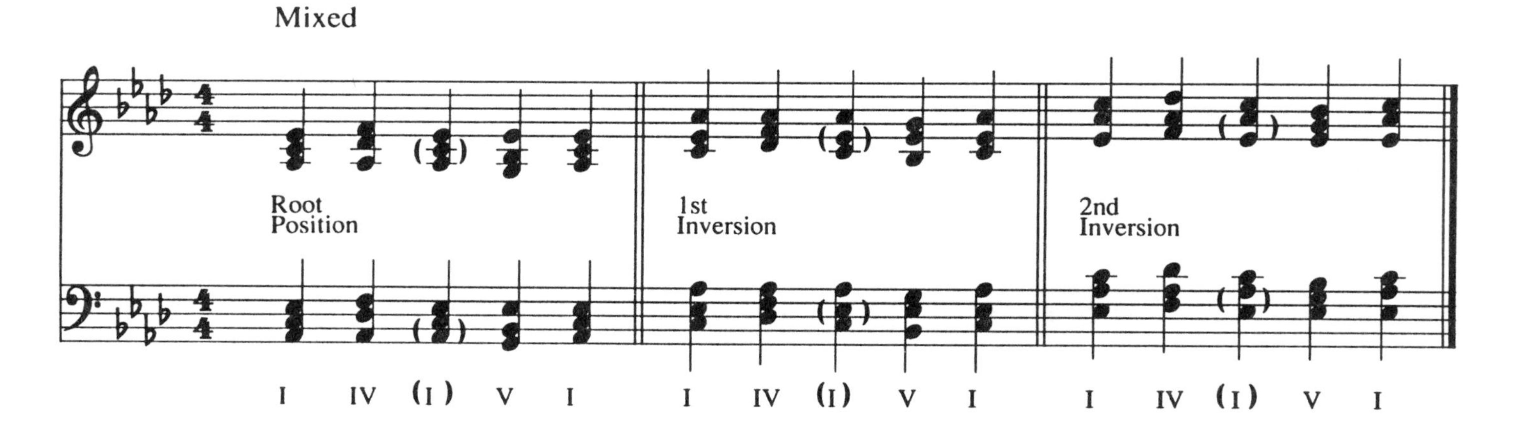
Mixed
Root Position
1st Inversion
2nd Inversion
I IV (I) V I
I IV (I) V I
I IV (I) V I

Key of A Flat (Major or Minor) Dominant Seventh Chords, Arpeggio and Cadence

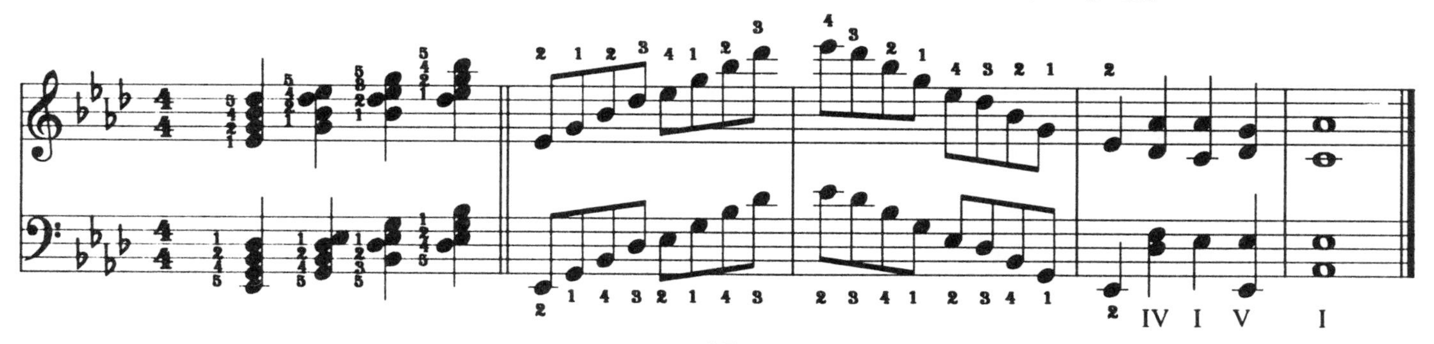
IV I V I

D Flat Major

D♭ Major Scale (1 Octave)

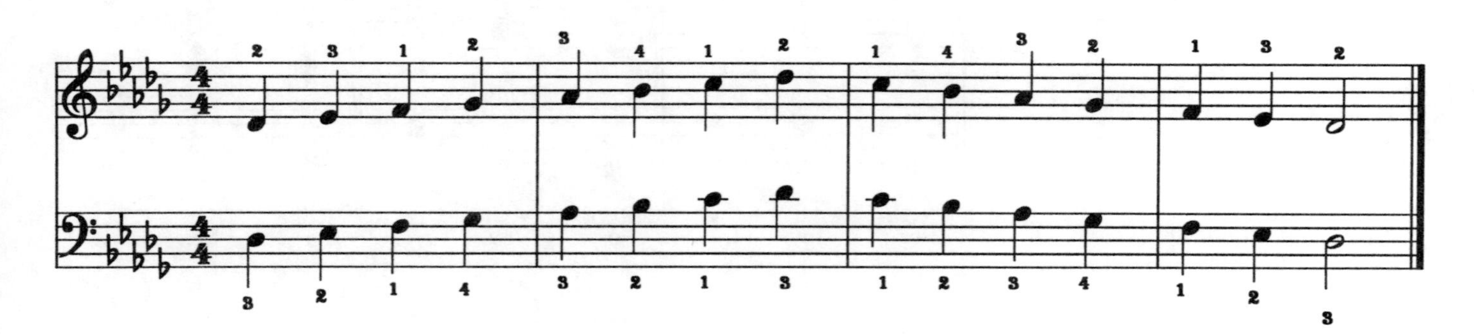

D♭ Major Scale (2 Octaves)

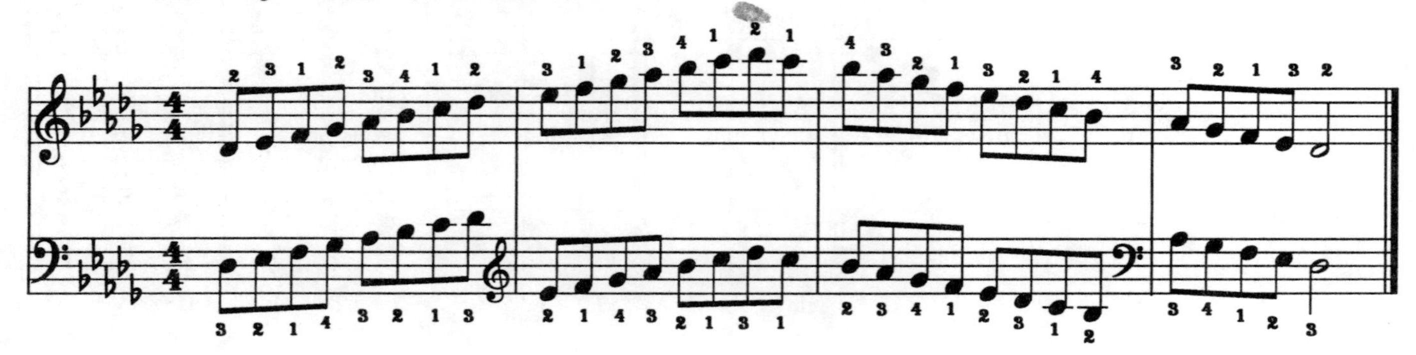

D♭ Major Arpeggio (1 Octave) D♭ Major Arpeggio (2 Octaves)

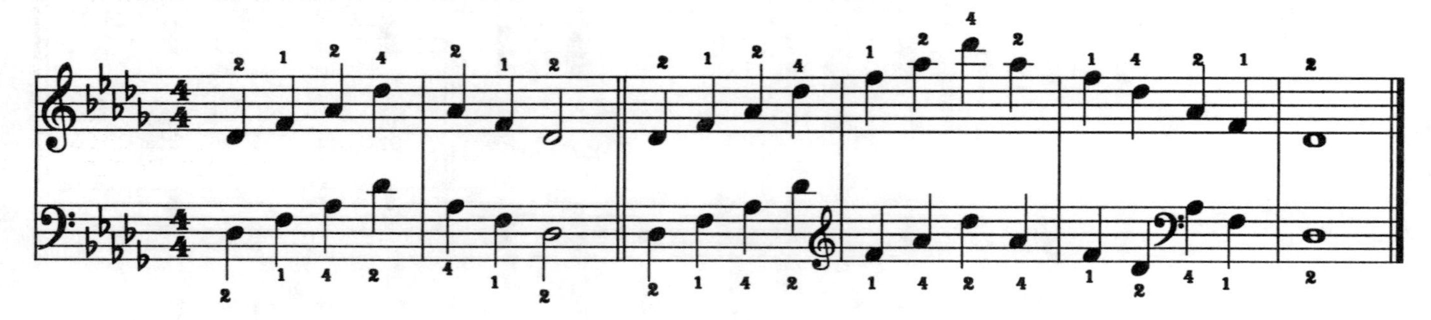

D♭ Major Arpeggios In Inversions

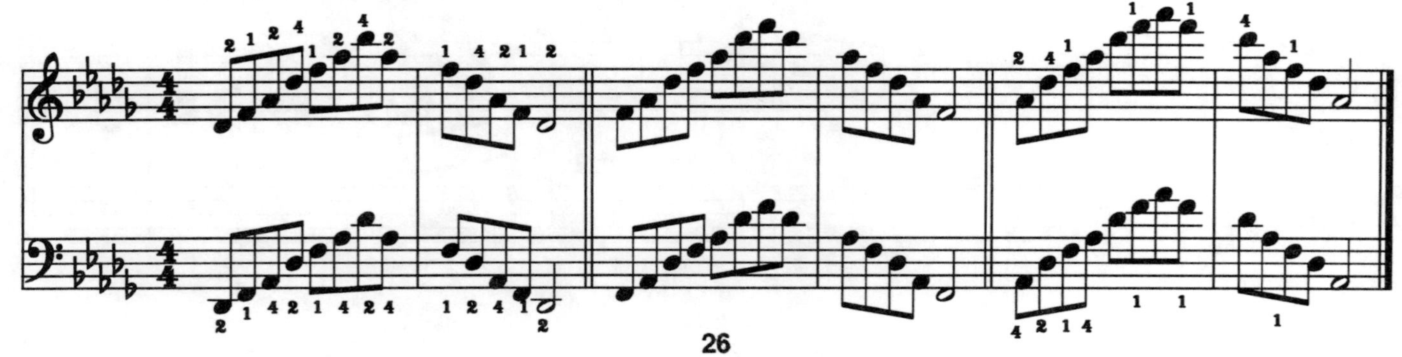

Inversions of Principal Chords of D♭ Major

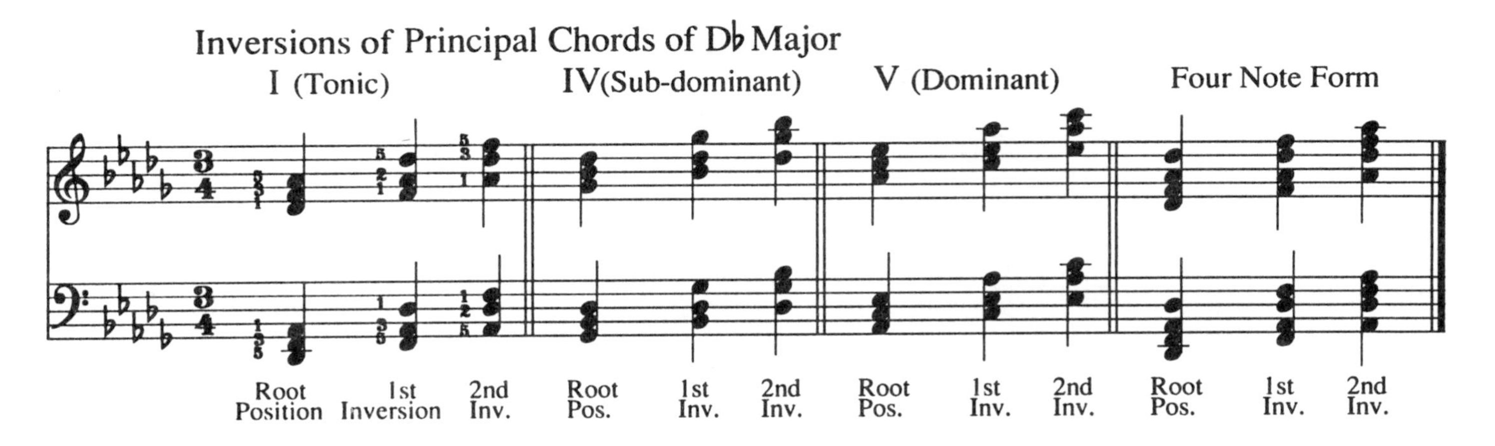
I (Tonic)
IV(Sub-dominant)
V (Dominant)
Four Note Form
Root Position
1st Inversion
2nd Inv.
Root Pos.
1st Inv.
2nd Inv.
Root Pos.
1st Inv.
2nd Inv.
Root Pos.
1st Inv.
2nd Inv.

Cadences In D♭ Major

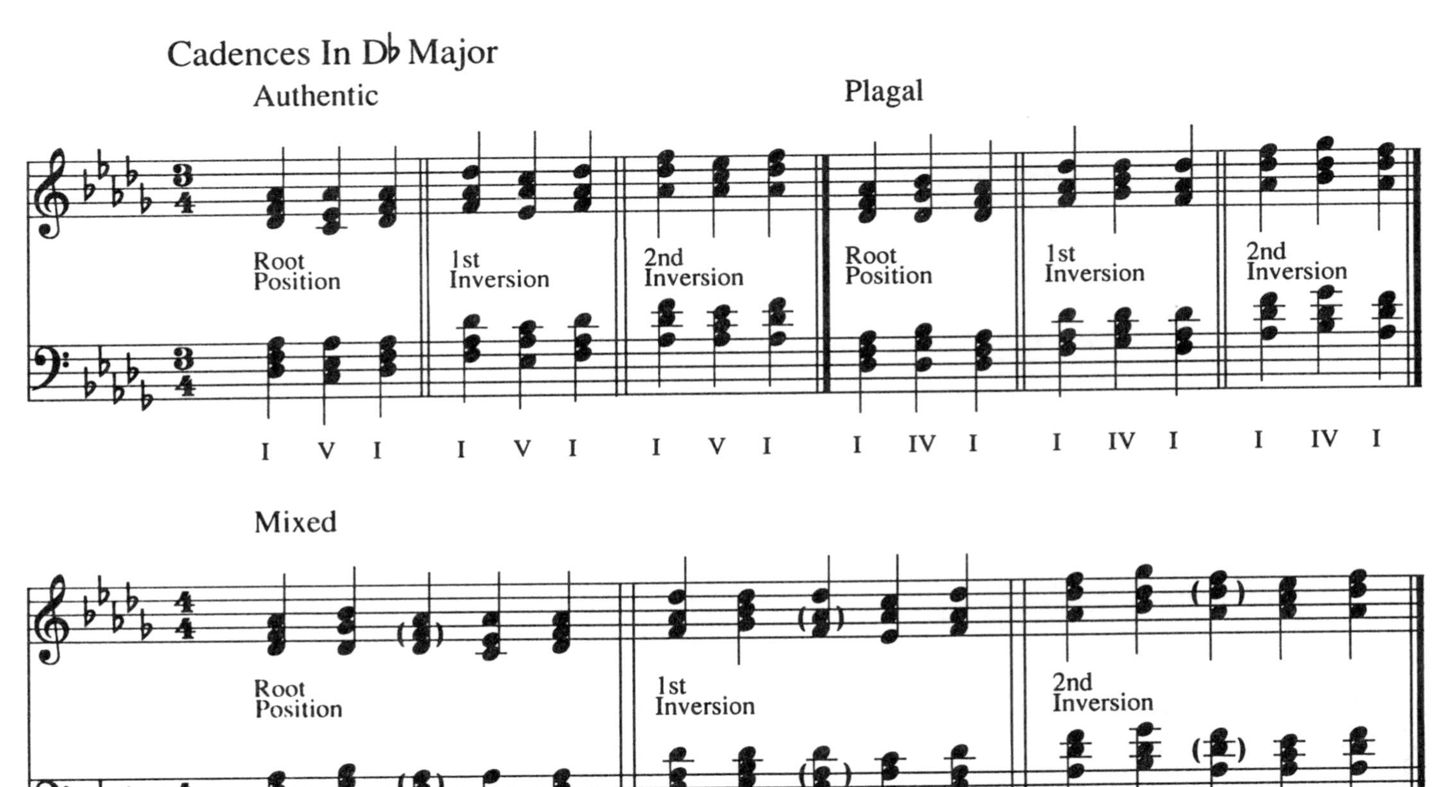
Authentic
Plagal
Root Position
1st Inversion
2nd Inversion
Root Position
1st Inversion
2nd Inversion
I V I
I V I
I V I
I IV I
I IV I
I IV I
Mixed
Root Position
1st Inversion
2nd Inversion
I IV (I) V I
I IV (I) V I
I IV (I) V I

Key of D Flat (Major or Minor) Dominant Seventh Chords, Arpeggio and Cadence

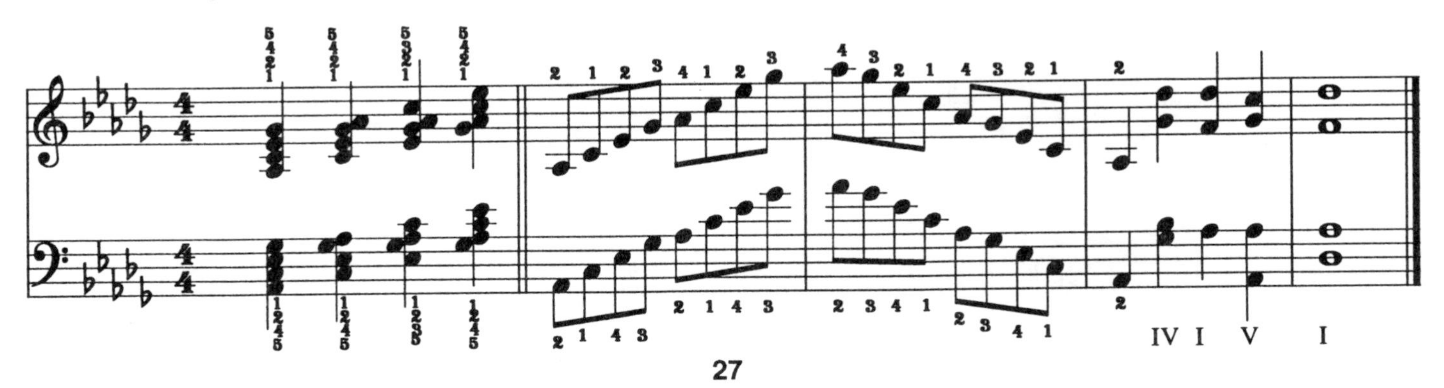
IV I V I

G Flat Major

G♭ Major Scale (1 Octave)

G♭ Major Scale (2 Octaves)

G♭ Major Arpeggio (1 Octave)   G♭ Major Arpeggio (2 Octaves)

G♭ Major Arpeggios In Inversions

Inversions of Principal Chords of G♭ Major

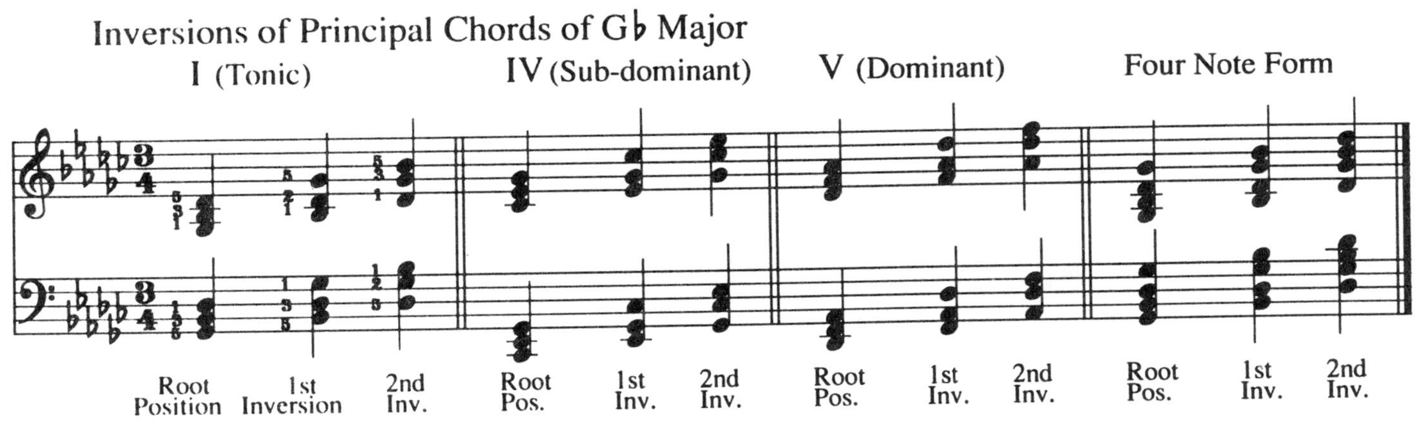
I (Tonic)
IV (Sub-dominant)
V (Dominant)
Four Note Form
Root Position
1st Inversion
2nd Inv.
Root Pos.
1st Inv.
2nd Inv.
Root Pos.
1st Inv.
2nd Inv.
Root Pos.
1st Inv.
2nd Inv.

Cadences In G♭ Major

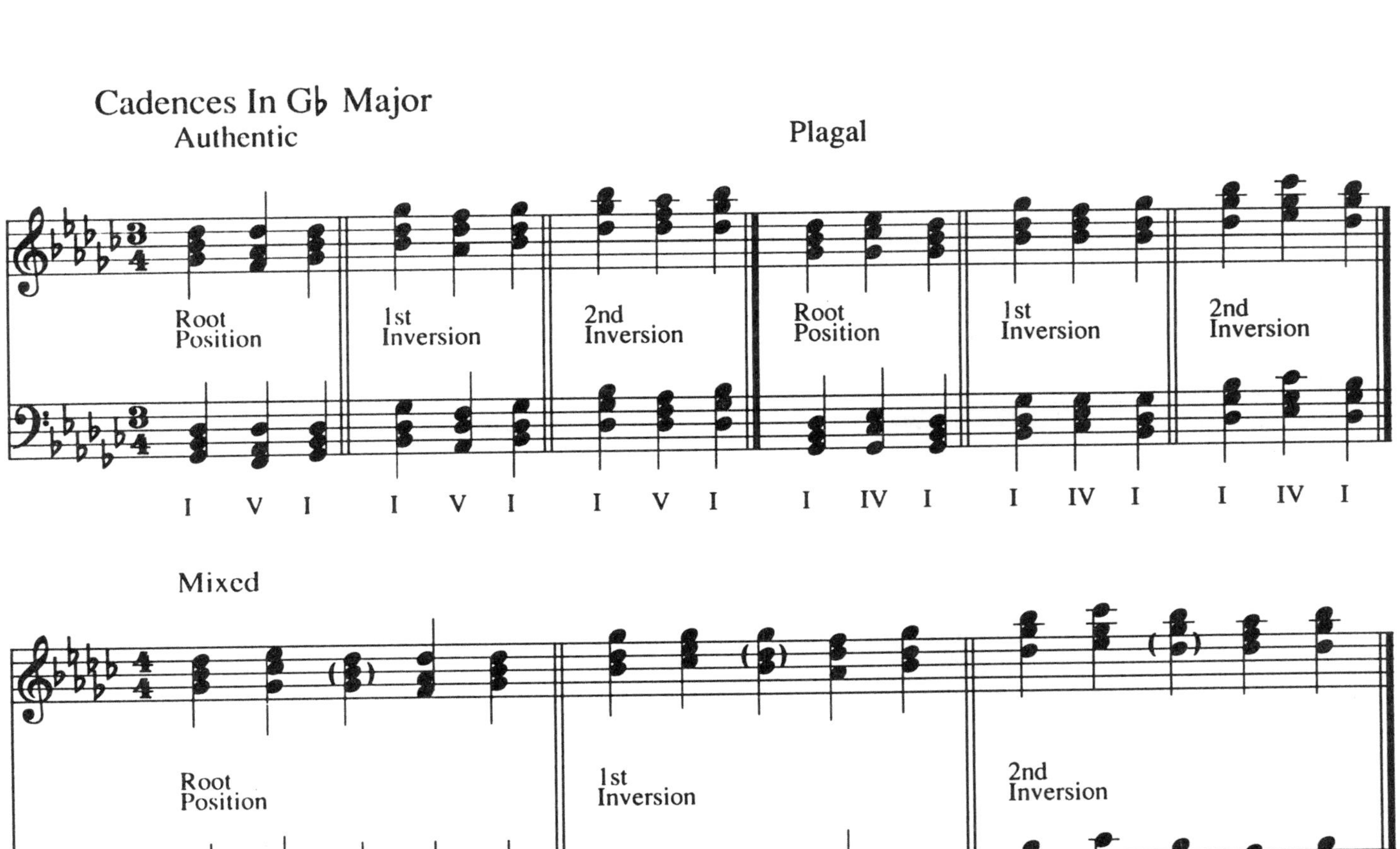
Authentic
Plagal
Root Position
1st Inversion
2nd Inversion
Root Position
1st Inversion
2nd Inversion
I V I
I V I
I V I
I IV I
I IV I
I IV I
Mixed
Root Position
1st Inversion
2nd Inversion
I IV (I) V I
I IV (I) V I
I IV (I) V I

Key of G Flat (Major or Minor) Dominant Seventh Chords, Arpeggio and Cadence

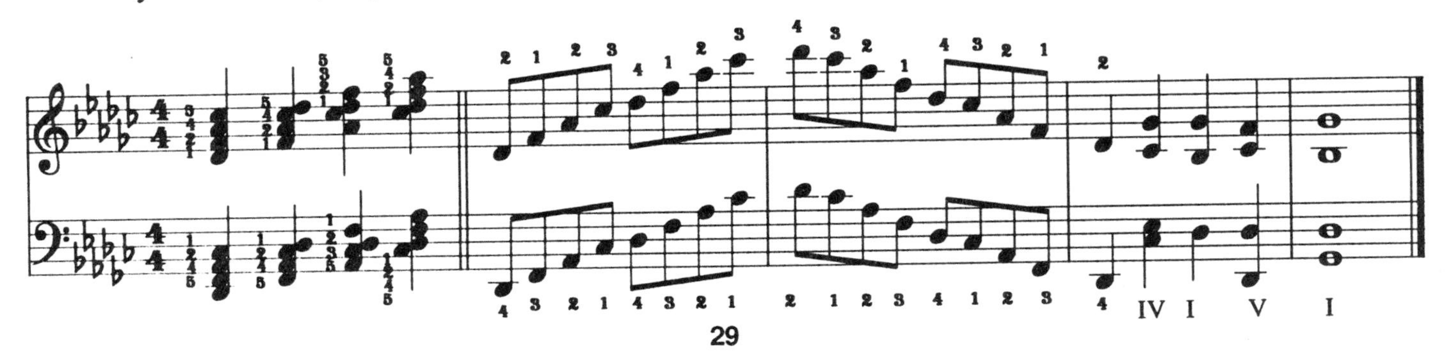
IV I V I

Minor Scales

The **Relative Minor Scale** is built on the sixth step of the Major Scale.

The **Natural Minor Scale** is the unaltered form of the Relative Minor Scale.

A Natural Minor Scale

6th step of the C Major Scale (A minor)

The **Harmonic Minor Scale** is formed by raising 7th tone of the Natural Minor Scale one half step.

A Harmonic Minor Scale

Tones 1 2 3 4 5 6 7 8 7 6 5 4 3 2 1

The **Melodic Minor Scale** is formed by raising the 6th & 7th tones of the Natural Minor Scale by one half step, while ascending only. While descending, the Natural Minor form is used.

A Melodic Minor Scale

Tones 1 2 3 4 5 6 7 8 7 6 5 4 3 2 1

The Circle of Fifths

The Circle of Fifths chart, detailed below, is a circular arrangement of the 12 keys in ascending or descending fifths: the sharps arranged from the top moving clockwise (ascending) and the flats arranged from the top moving counterclockwise (descending). The Relative Keys, major and minor keys having the same Key Signature, are shown together on the circle. The keys at the bottom of the circle are the **Enharmonic Keys**, which have the same sound while having two different names.

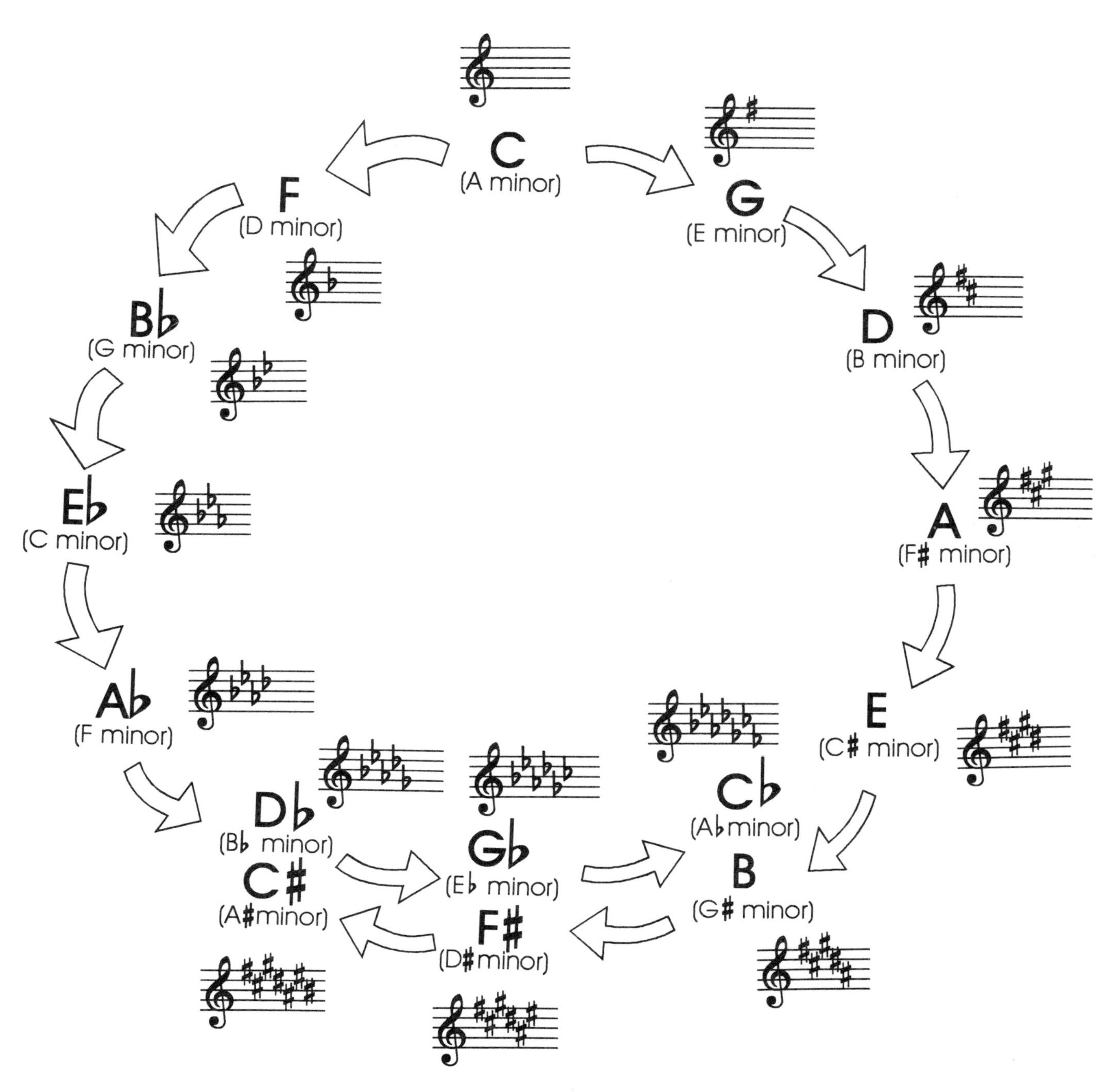

C
(A minor)
G
(E minor)
D
(B minor)
A
(F# minor)
E
(C# minor)
Cb
(Ab minor)
B
(G# minor)
Gb
(Eb minor)
F#
(D# minor)
Db
(Bb minor)
C#
(A# minor)
Ab
(F minor)
Eb
(C minor)
Bb
(G minor)
F
(D minor)

A Minor

(Relative Minor to C Major)

A Harmonic Minor Scale (1 Octave)

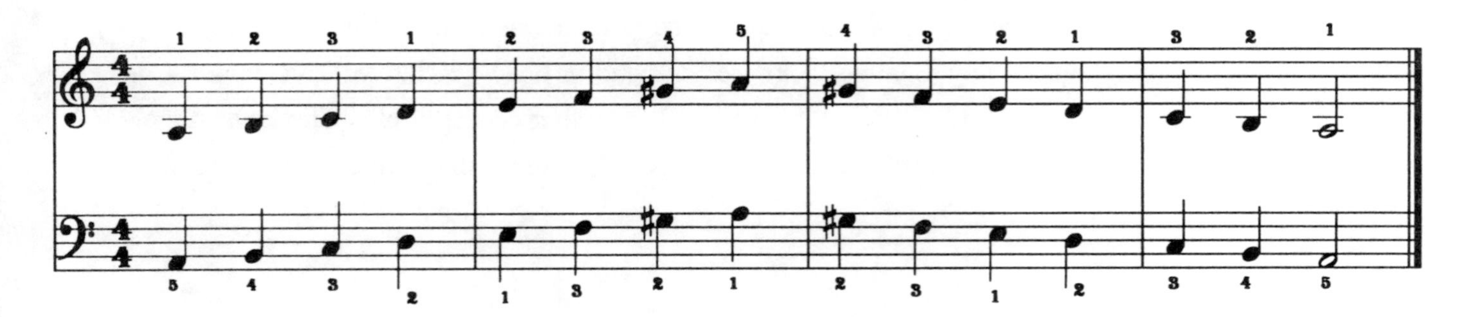

A Harmonic Minor Scale (2 Octave)

A Minor Arpeggio (1 Octave) A Minor Arpeggio (2 Octaves)

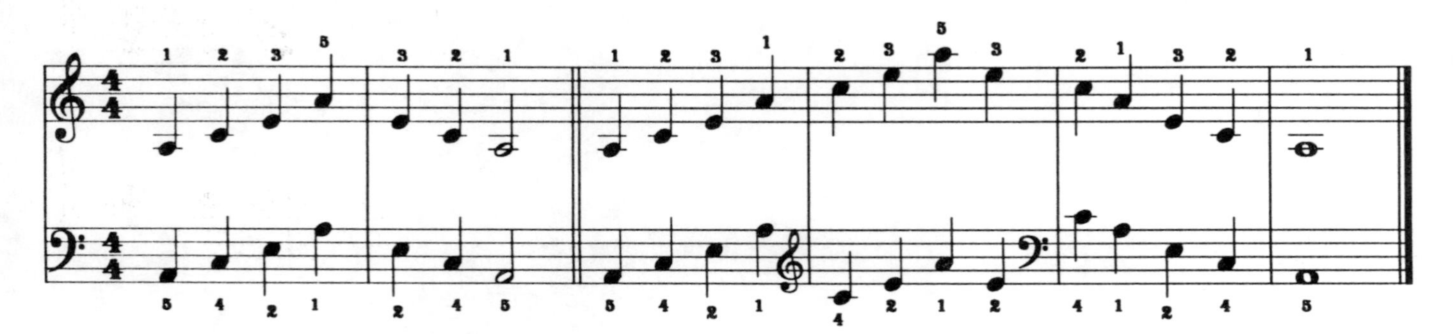

A Minor Arpeggios In Inversions

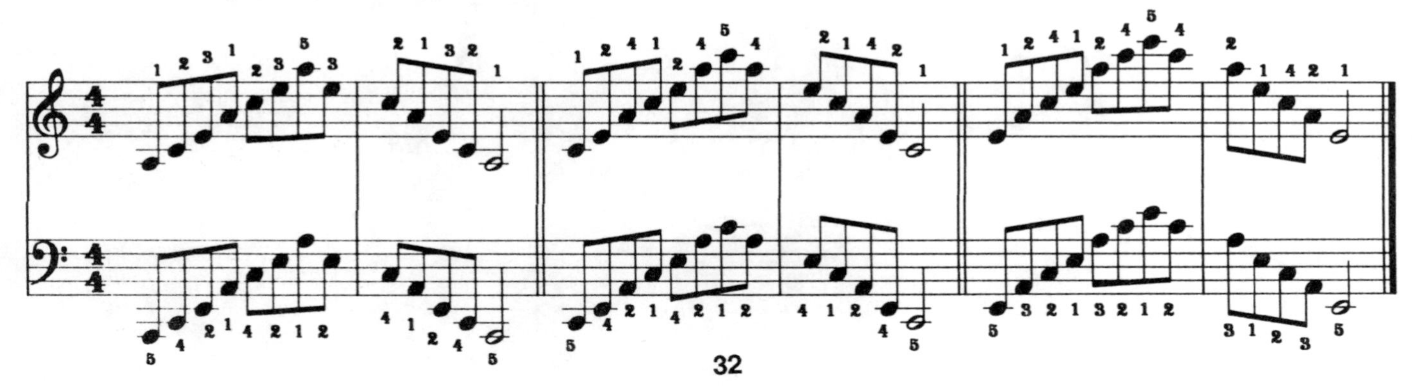

Inversions of Principal Chords of A Minor

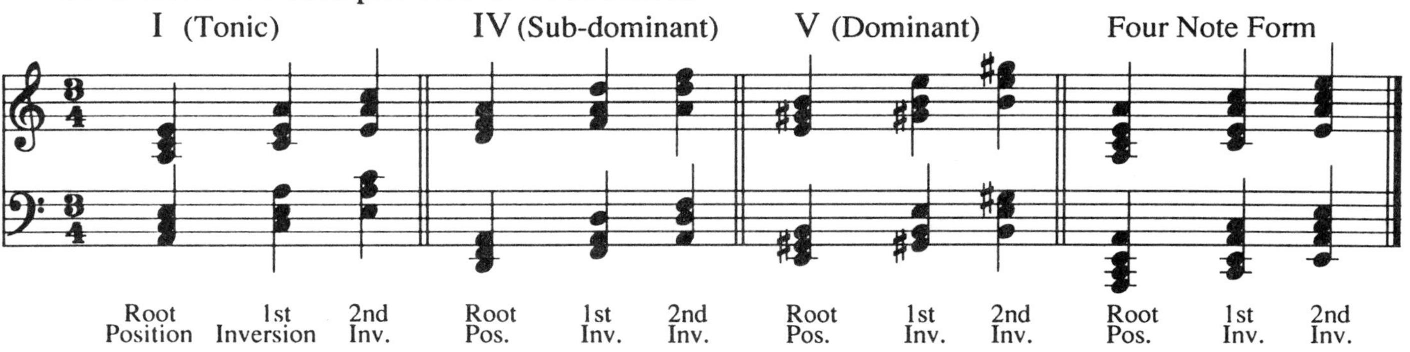
I (Tonic)
IV (Sub-dominant)
V (Dominant)
Four Note Form
Root Position
1st Inversion
2nd Inv.
Root Pos.
1st Inv.
2nd Inv.
Root Pos.
1st Inv.
2nd Inv.
Root Pos.
1st Inv.
2nd Inv.

Cadences In A Minor

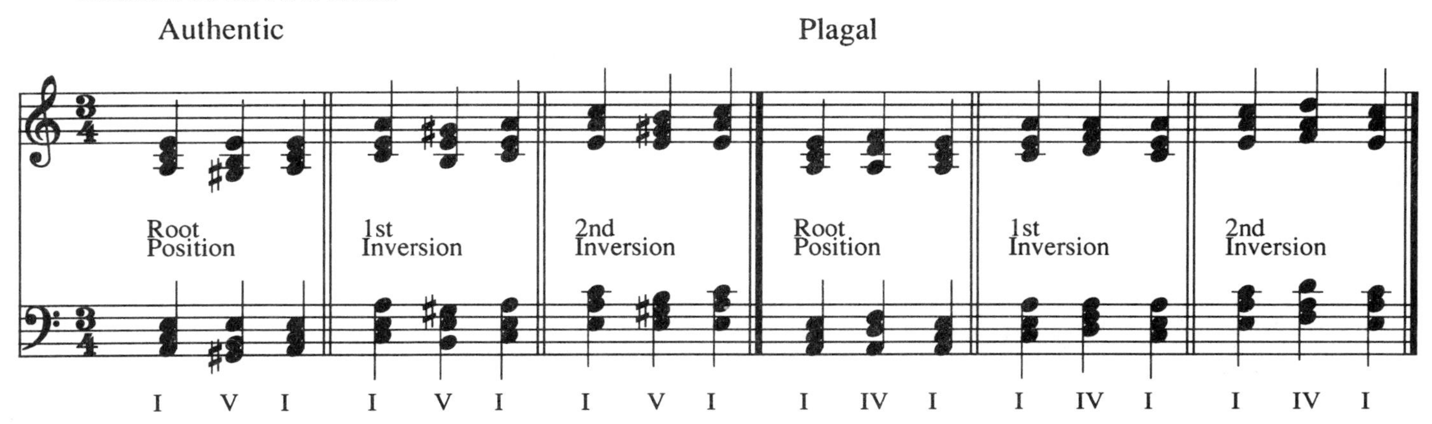
Authentic
Plagal
Root Position
1st Inversion
2nd Inversion
Root Position
1st Inversion
2nd Inversion
I V I
I V I
I V I
I IV I
I IV I
I IV I

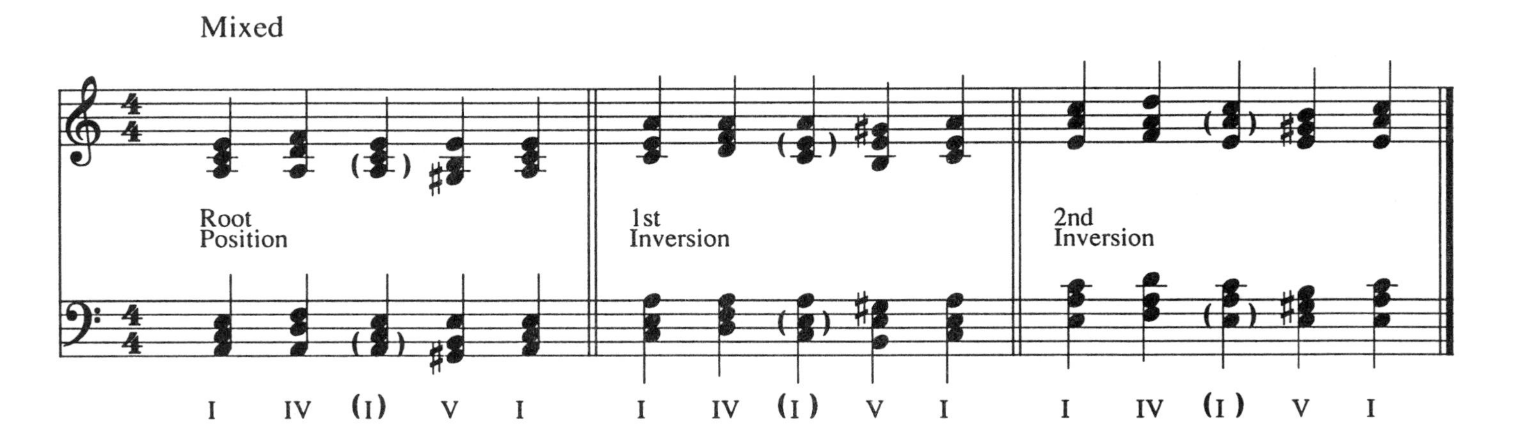
Mixed
Root Position
1st Inversion
2nd Inversion
I IV (I) V I
I IV (I) V I
I IV (I) V I

A Melodic Minor Scale (2 Octave)

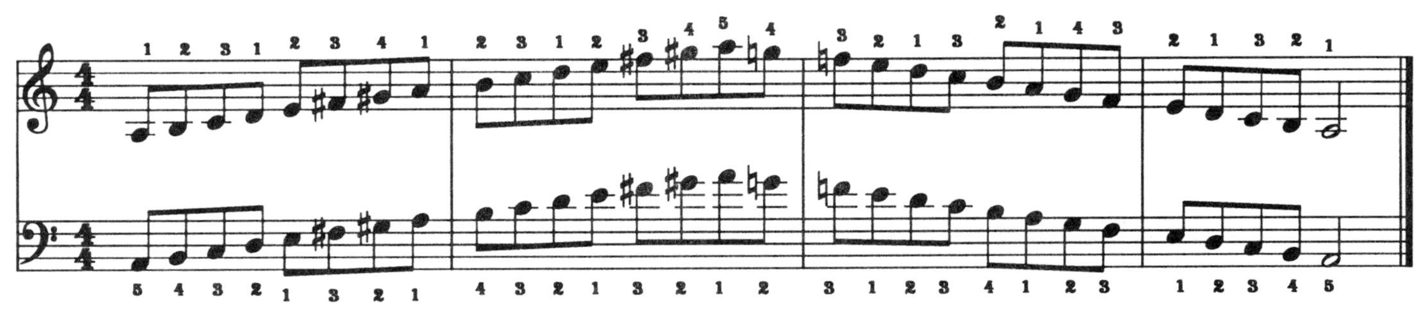

E Minor

(Relative Minor to G Major)

E Harmonic Minor Scale (1 Octave)

E Harmonic Minor Scale (2 Octave)

E Minor Arpeggio (1 Octave) E Minor Arpeggio (2 Octaves)

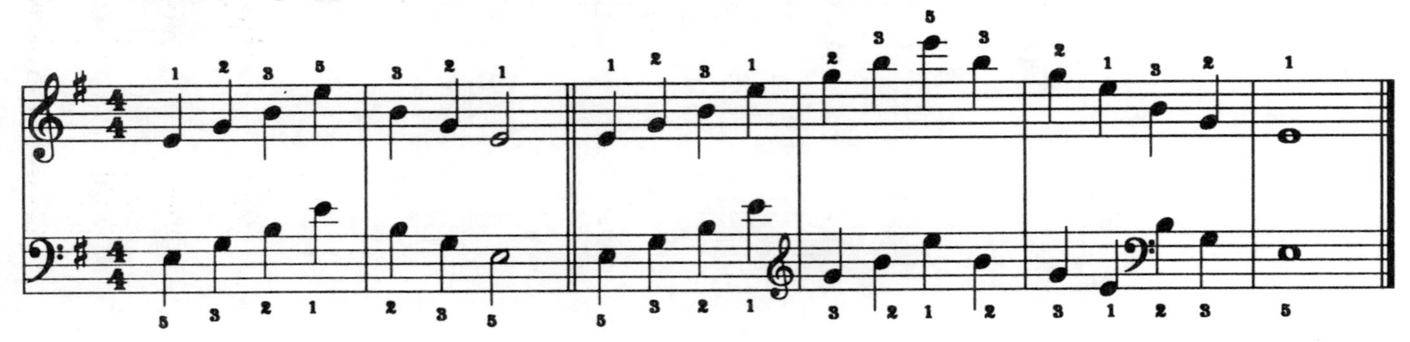

E Minor Arpeggios In Inversions

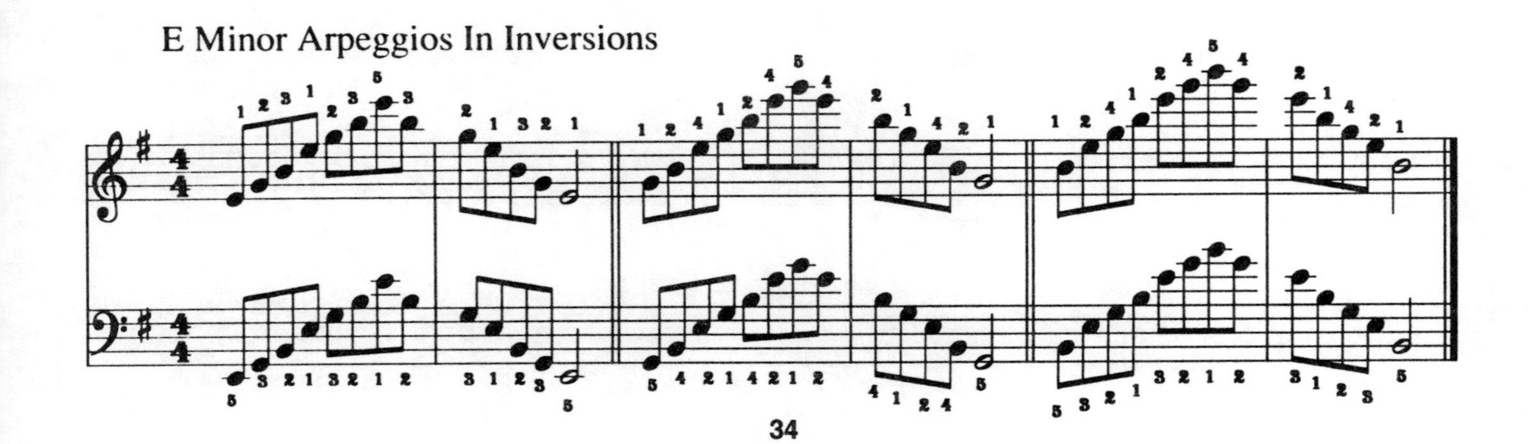

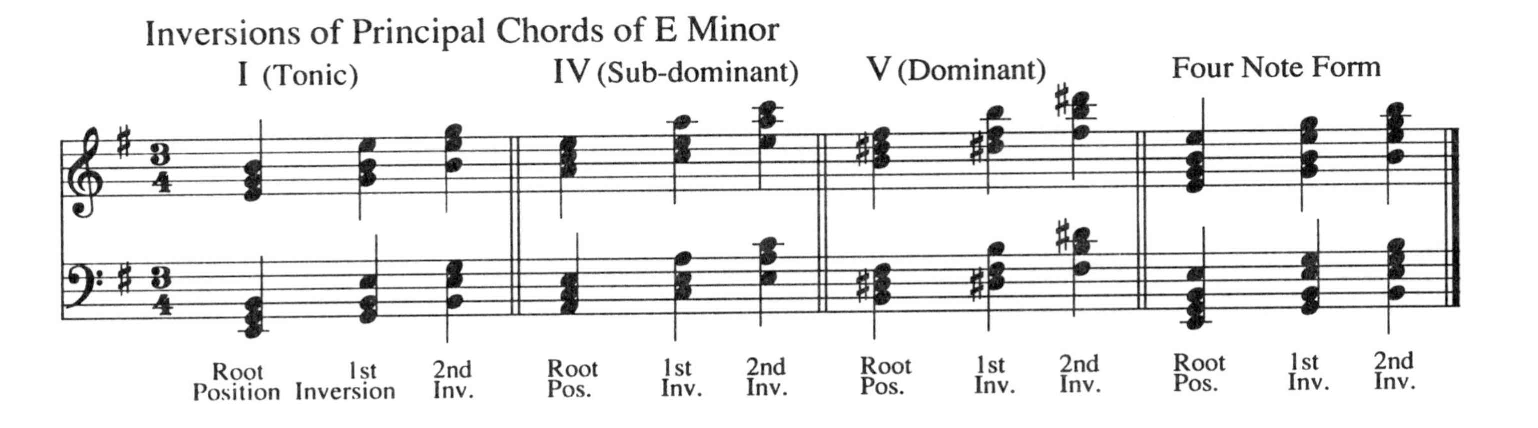
Inversions of Principal Chords of E Minor
I (Tonic)
IV (Sub-dominant)
V (Dominant)
Four Note Form
Root Position
1st Inversion
2nd Inv.
Root Pos.
1st Inv.
2nd Inv.
Root Pos.
1st Inv.
2nd Inv.
Root Pos.
1st Inv.
2nd Inv.

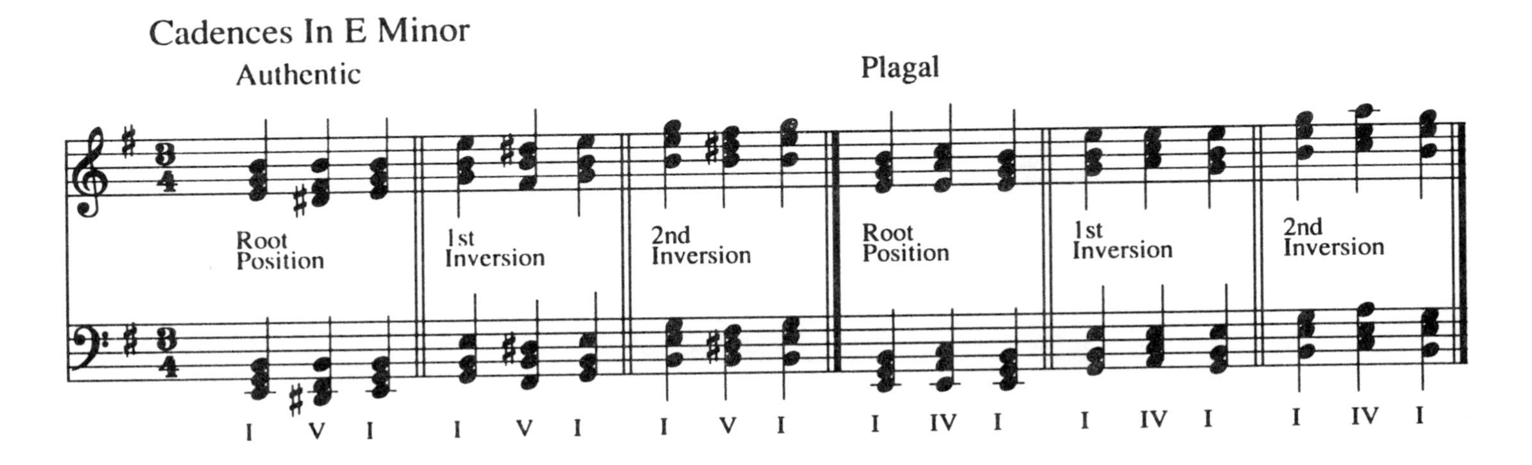
Cadences In E Minor
Authentic
Plagal
Root Position
1st Inversion
2nd Inversion
Root Position
1st Inversion
2nd Inversion
I V I
I V I
I V I
I IV I
I IV I
I IV I

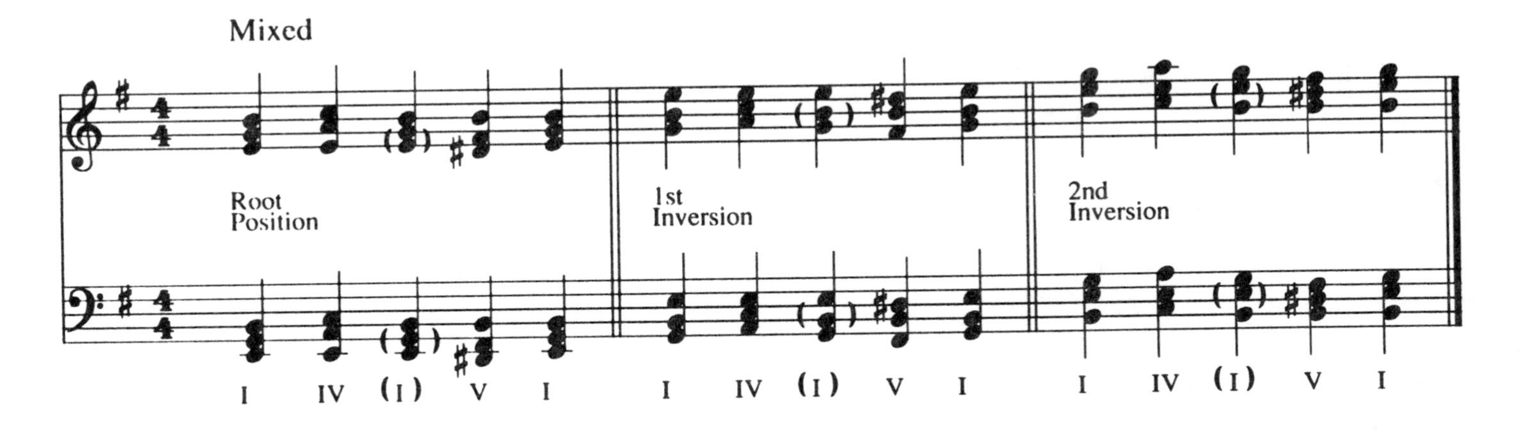
Mixed
Root Position
1st Inversion
2nd Inversion
I IV (I) V I
I IV (I) V I
I IV (I) V I

E Melodic Minor Scale (2 Octave)

B Minor
(Relative Minor to D Major)

B Harmonic Minor Scale (1 Octave)

B Harmonic Minor Scale (2 Octave)

B Minor Arpeggio (1 Octave) B Minor Arpeggio (2 Octaves)

B Minor Arpeggios In Inversions

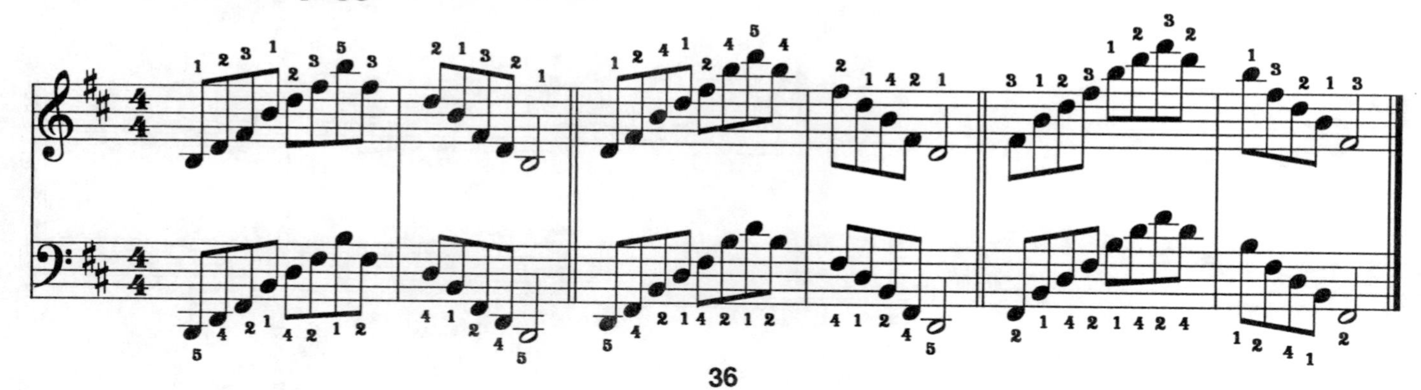

Inversions of Principal Chords of B Minor

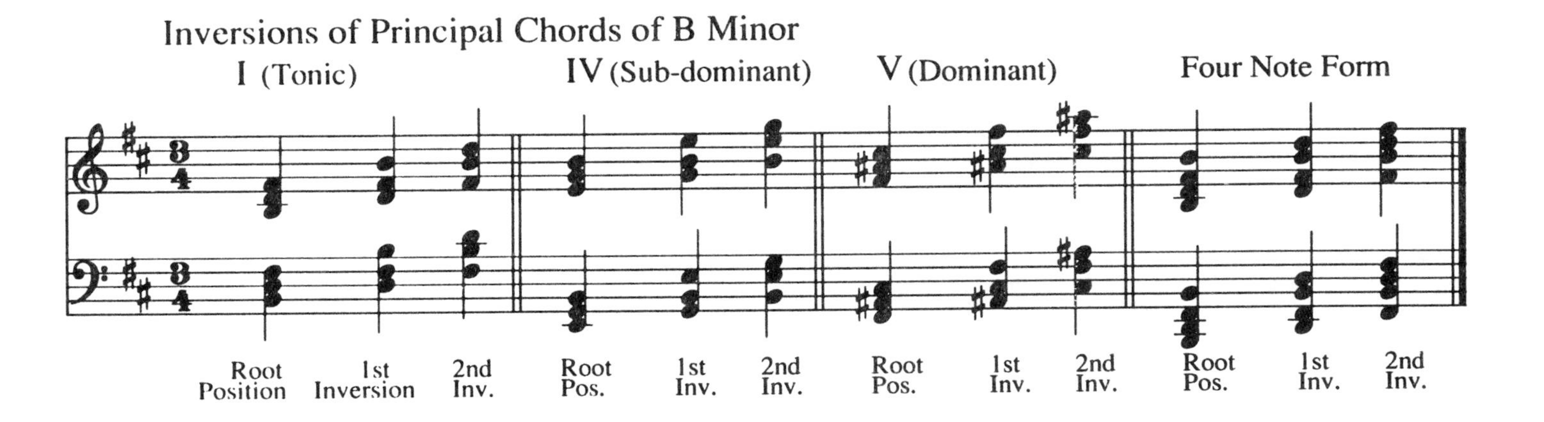
I (Tonic)
IV (Sub-dominant)
V (Dominant)
Four Note Form
Root Position
1st Inversion
2nd Inv.
Root Pos.
1st Inv.
2nd Inv.
Root Pos.
1st Inv.
2nd Inv.
Root Pos.
1st Inv.
2nd Inv.

Cadences In B Minor

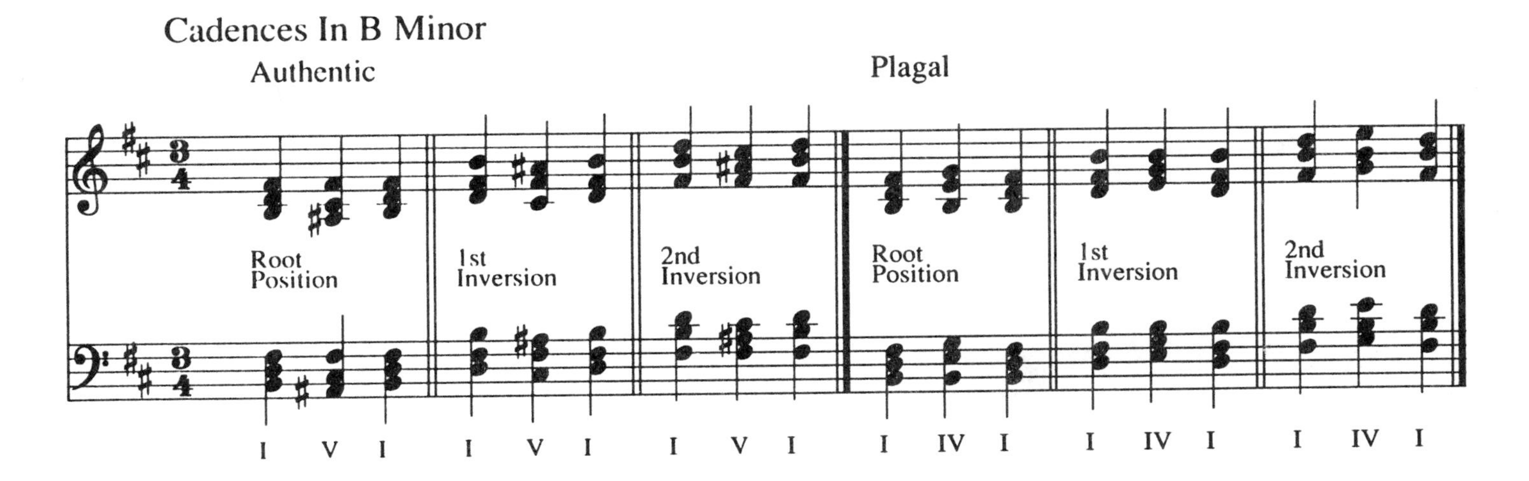
Authentic
Plagal
Root Position
1st Inversion
2nd Inversion
Root Position
1st Inversion
2nd Inversion
I V I
I V I
I V I
I IV I
I IV I
I IV I

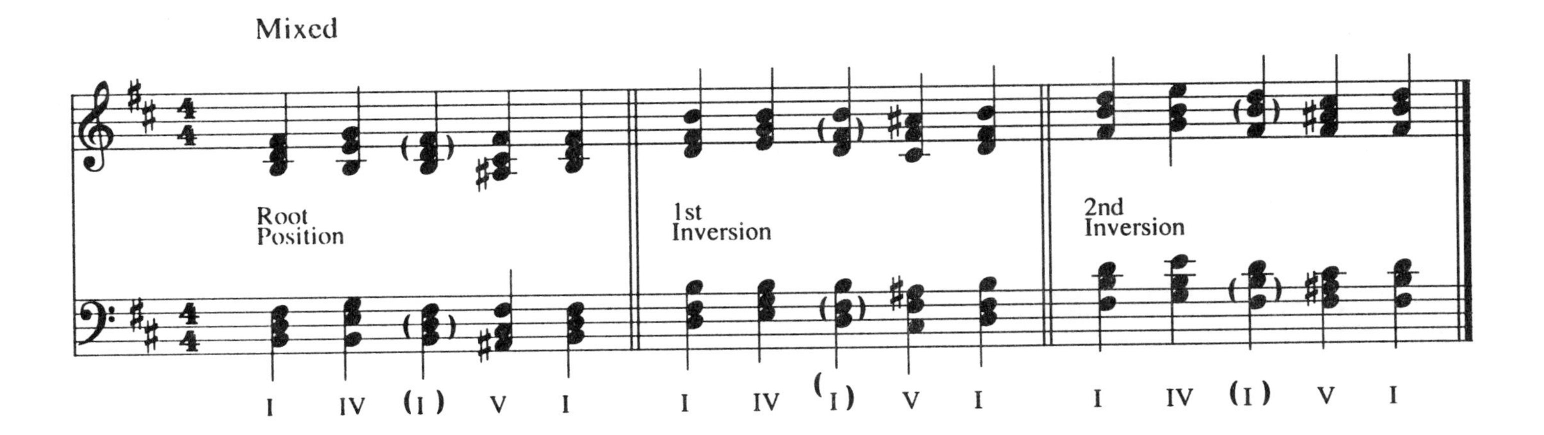
Mixed
Root Position
1st Inversion
2nd Inversion
I IV (I) V I
I IV (I) V I
I IV (I) V I

B Melodic Minor Scale (2 Octave)

F Sharp Minor

(Relative Minor to A Major)

F♯ Harmonic Minor Scale (1 Octave)

F♯ Harmonic Minor Scale (2 Octave)

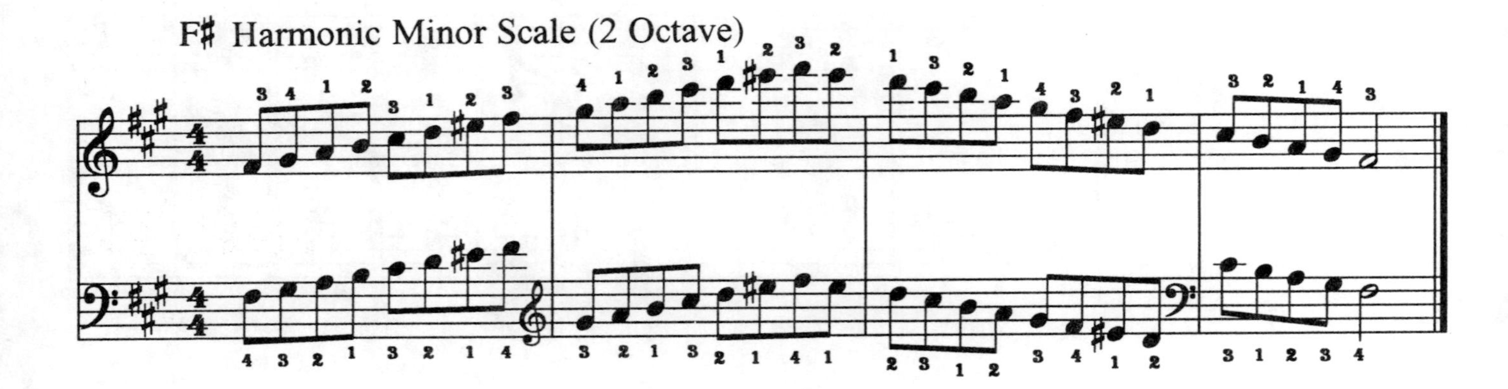

F♯ Minor Arpeggio (1 Octave) F♯ Minor Arpeggio (2 Octaves)

F♯ Minor Arpeggios In Inversions

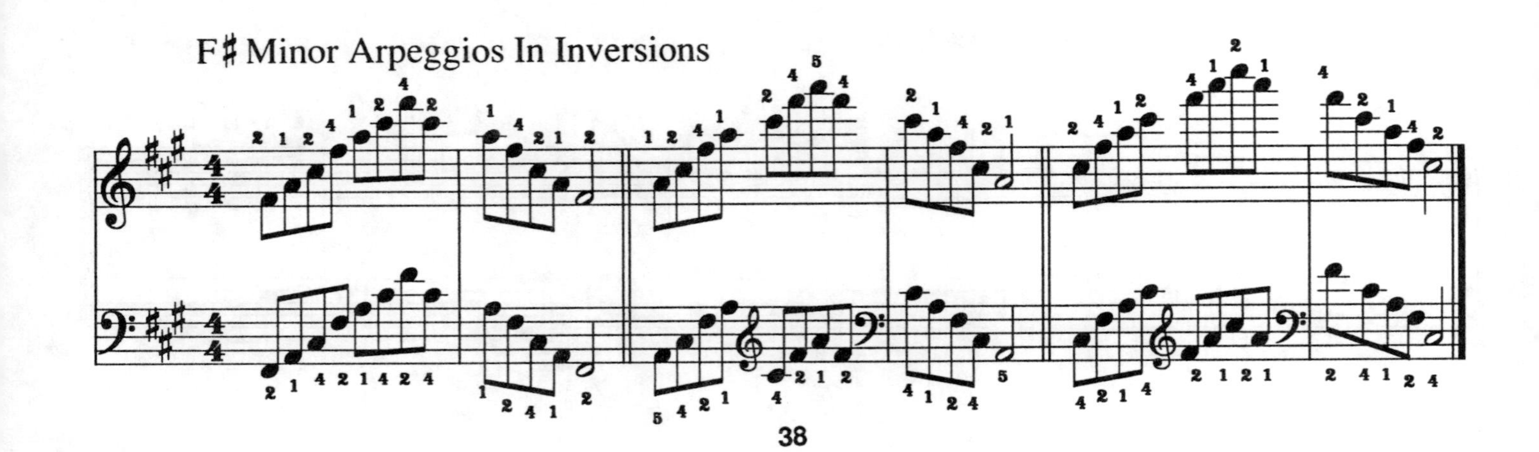

Inversions of Principal Chords of F♯ Minor

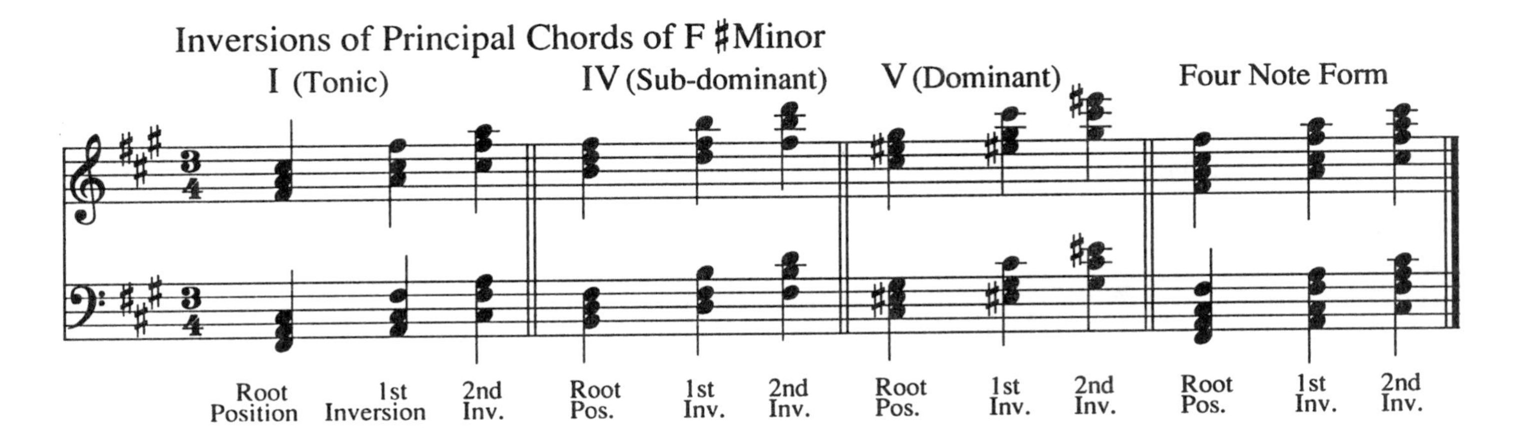
I (Tonic)
IV (Sub-dominant)
V (Dominant)
Four Note Form
Root Position
1st Inversion
2nd Inv.
Root Pos.
1st Inv.
2nd Inv.
Root Pos.
1st Inv.
2nd Inv.
Root Pos.
1st Inv.
2nd Inv.

Cadences In F♯ Minor

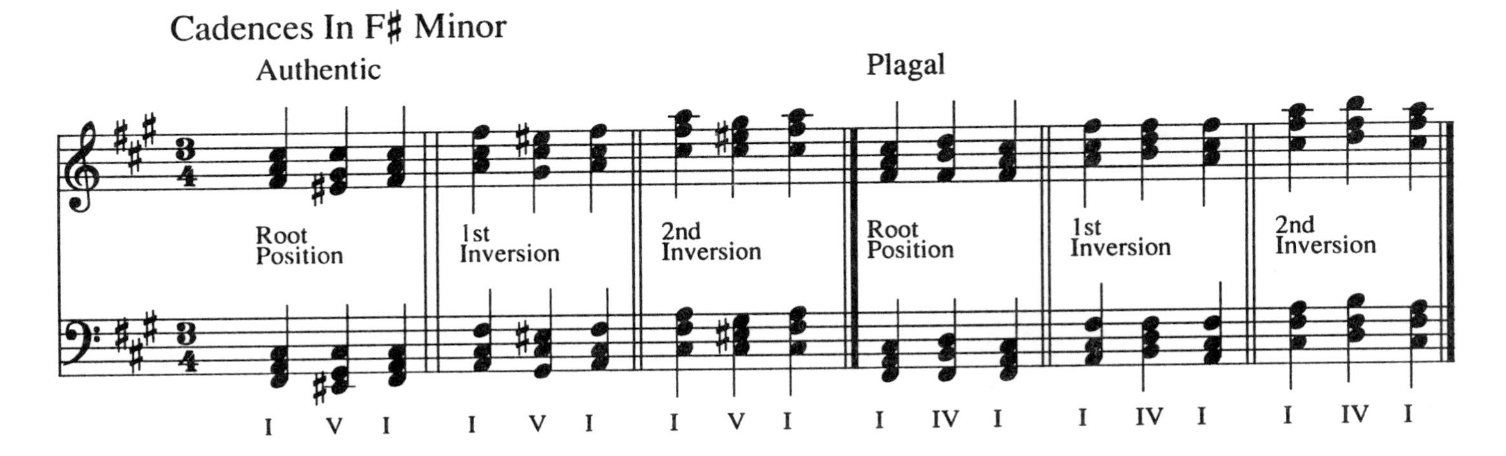
Authentic
Plagal
Root Position
1st Inversion
2nd Inversion
Root Position
1st Inversion
2nd Inversion
I V I
I V I
I V I
I IV I
I IV I
I IV I

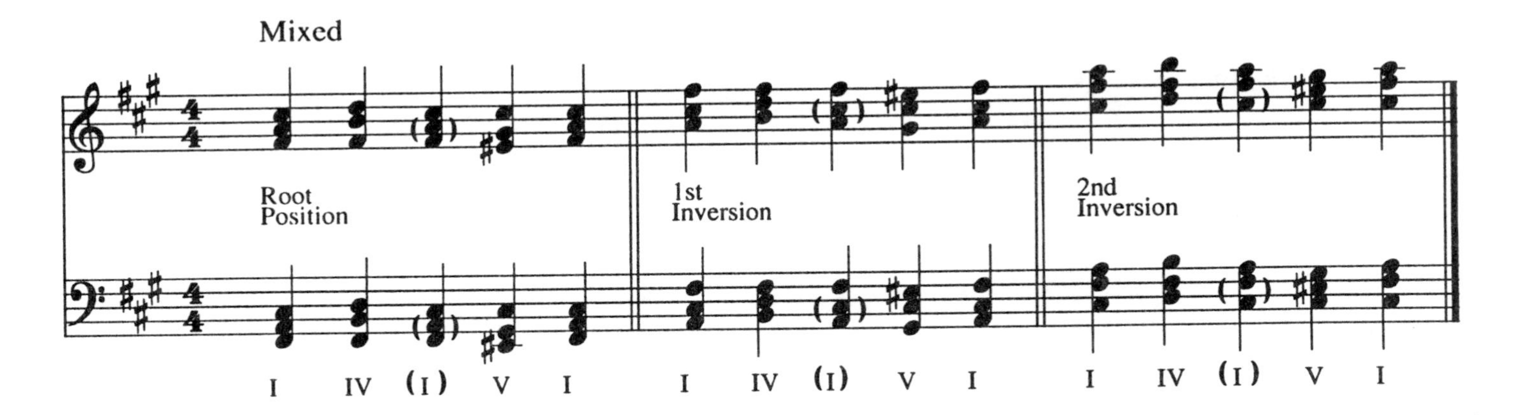
Mixed
Root Position
1st Inversion
2nd Inversion
I IV (I) V I
I IV (I) V I
I IV (I) V I

F Sharp Melodic Minor Scale (2 Octave)

C Sharp Minor

(Relative Minor to E Major)

C♯ Harmonic Minor Scale (1 Octave)

C♯ Harmonic Minor Scale (2 Octave)

C♯ Minor Arpeggio (1 Octave) C ♯Minor Arpeggio (2 Octaves)

C♯Minor Arpeggios In Inversions

Inversions of Principal Chords of C♯ Minor

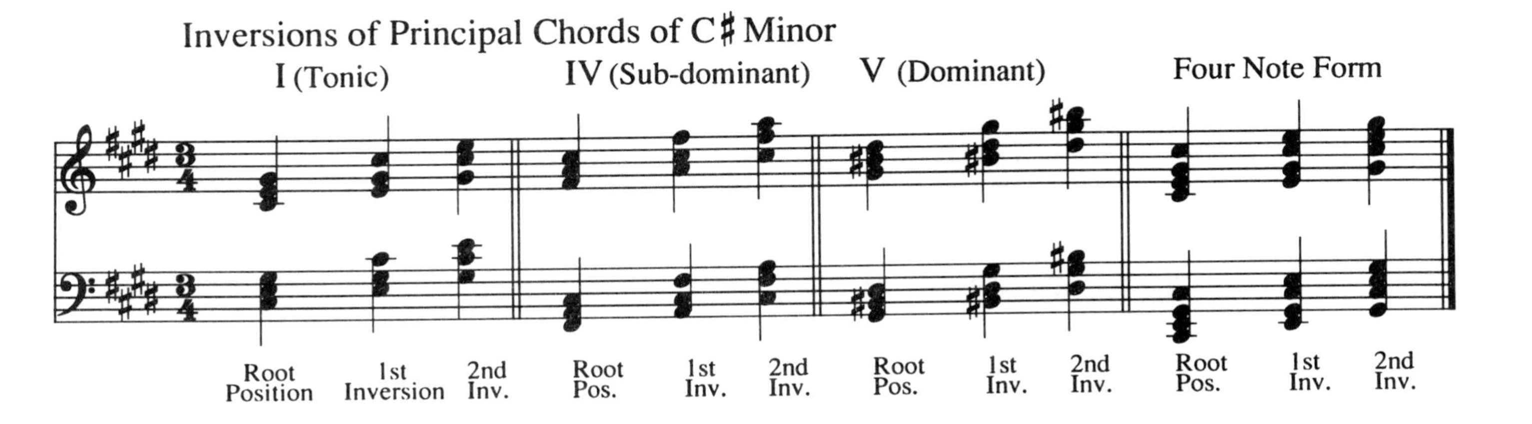
I (Tonic)
IV (Sub-dominant)
V (Dominant)
Four Note Form
Root Position
1st Inversion
2nd Inv.
Root Pos.
1st Inv.
2nd Inv.
Root Pos.
1st Inv.
2nd Inv.
Root Pos.
1st Inv.
2nd Inv.

Cadences In C♯ Minor

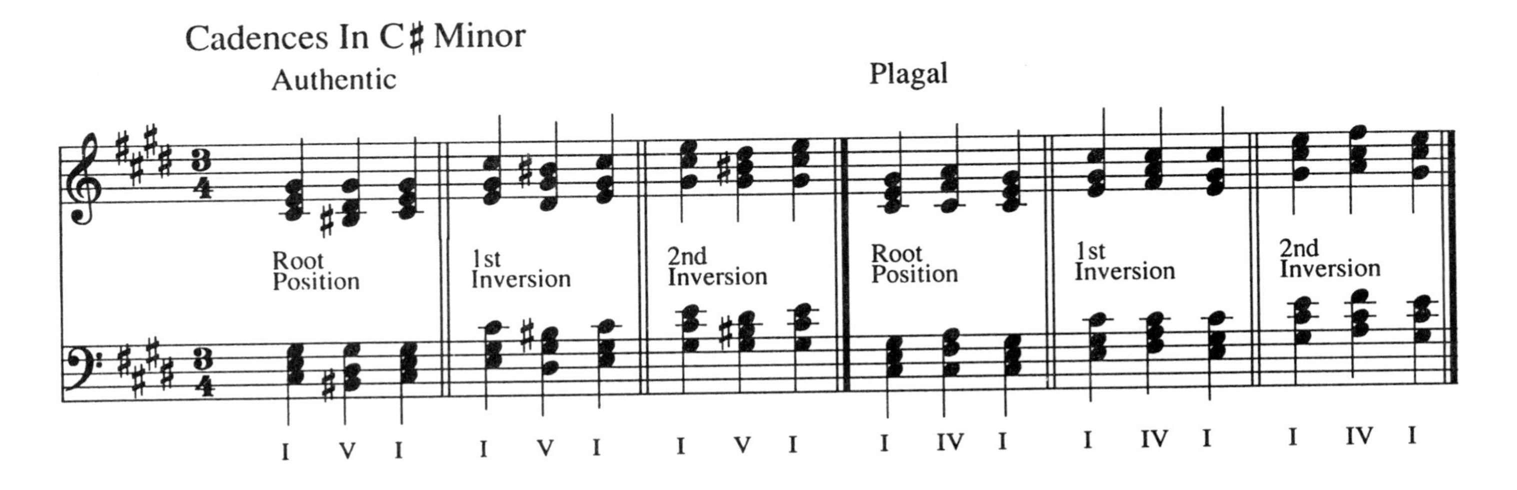
Authentic
Plagal
Root Position
1st Inversion
2nd Inversion
Root Position
1st Inversion
2nd Inversion
I V I
I V I
I V I
I IV I
I IV I
I IV I

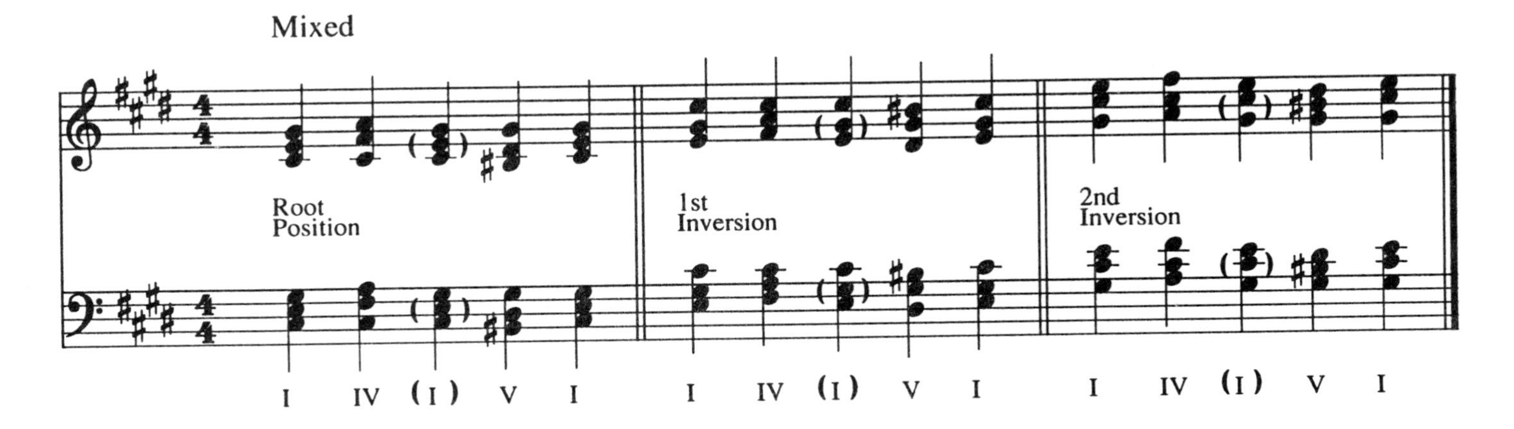
Mixed
Root Position
1st Inversion
2nd Inversion
I IV (I) V I
I IV (I) V I
I IV (I) V I

C Sharp Melodic Minor Scale (2 Octave)

G Sharp Minor

(Relative Minor to B Major)

G♯ Harmonic Minor Scale (1 Octave)

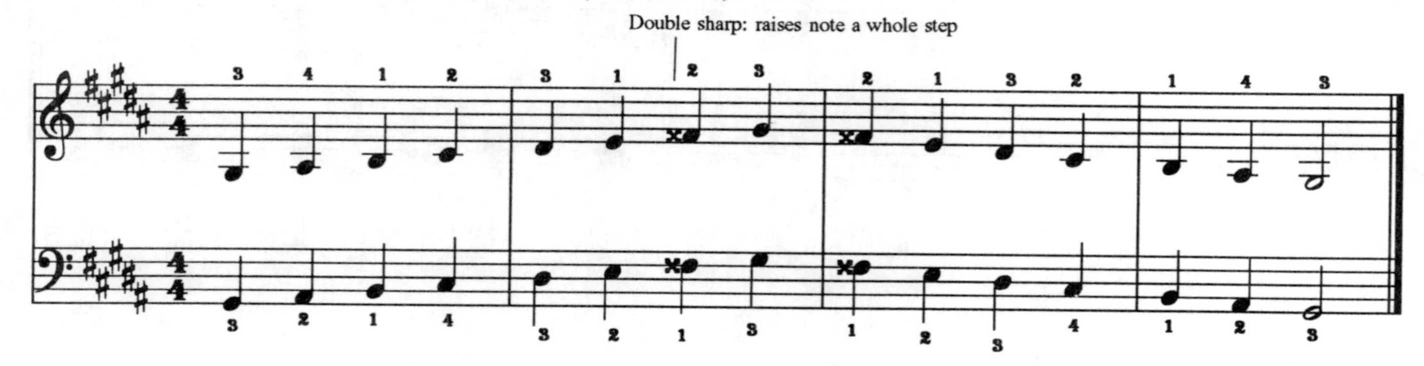
Double sharp: raises note a whole step

G♯ Harmonic Minor Scale (2 Octave)

G♯ Minor Arpeggio (1 Octave) G ♯Minor Arpeggio (2 Octaves)

G♯ Minor Arpeggios In Inversions

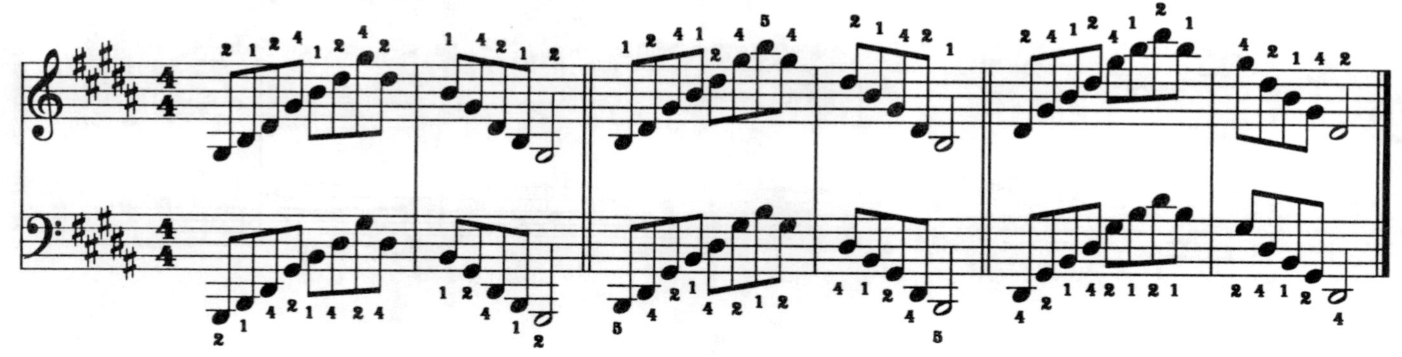

Inversions of Principal Chords of G♯ Minor

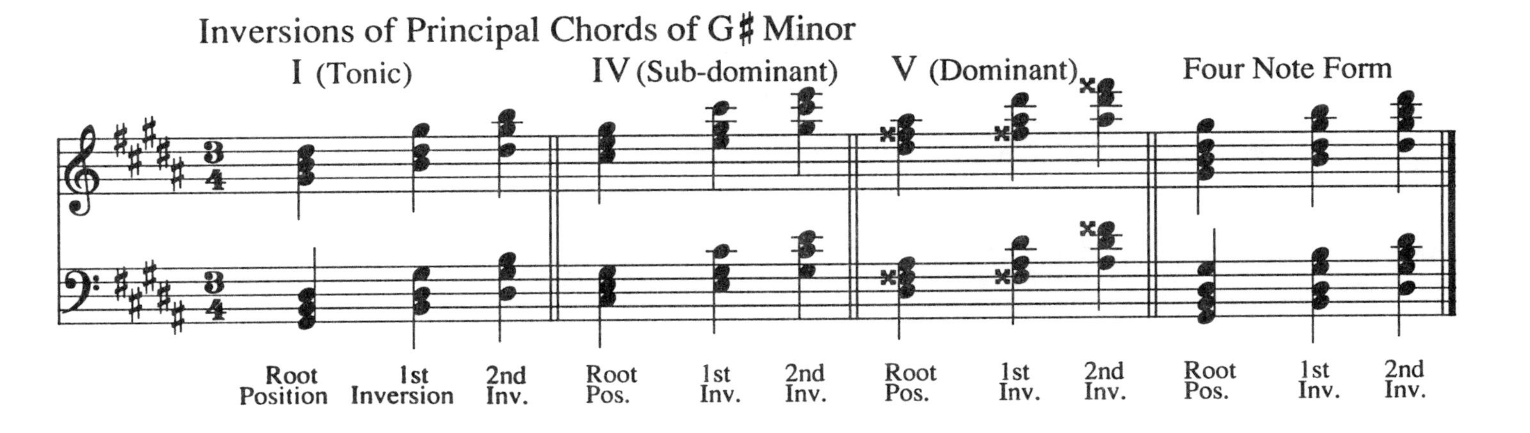
I (Tonic)
IV (Sub-dominant)
V (Dominant)
Four Note Form
Root Position
1st Inversion
2nd Inv.
Root Pos.
1st Inv.
2nd Inv.
Root Pos.
1st Inv.
2nd Inv.
Root Pos.
1st Inv.
2nd Inv.

Cadences In G♯ Minor

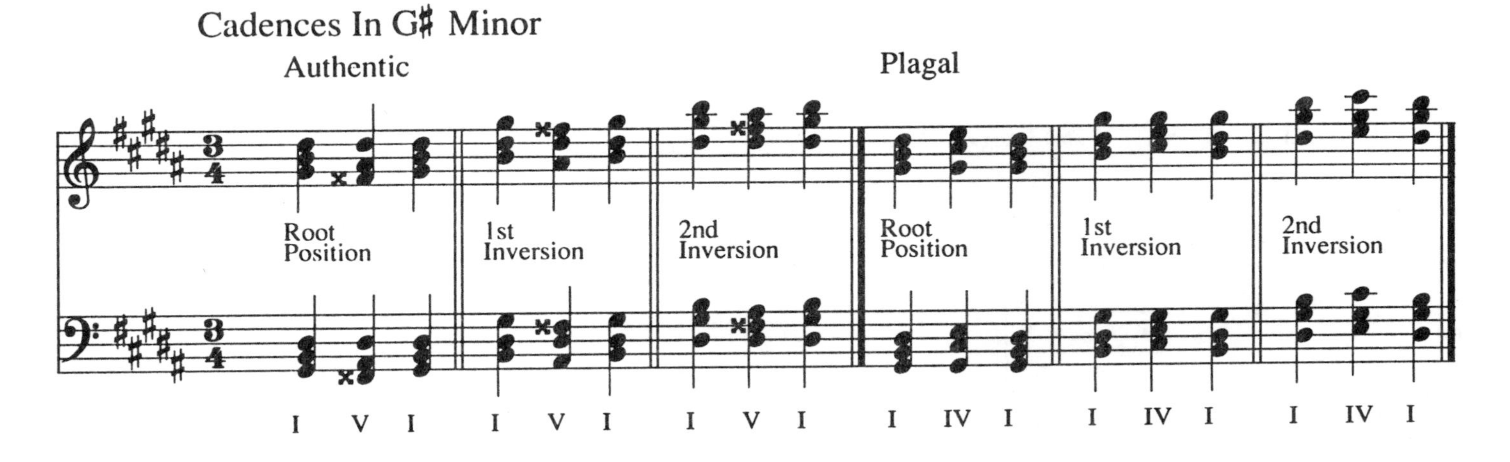
Authentic
Plagal
Root Position
1st Inversion
2nd Inversion
Root Position
1st Inversion
2nd Inversion
I V I
I V I
I V I
I IV I
I IV I
I IV I

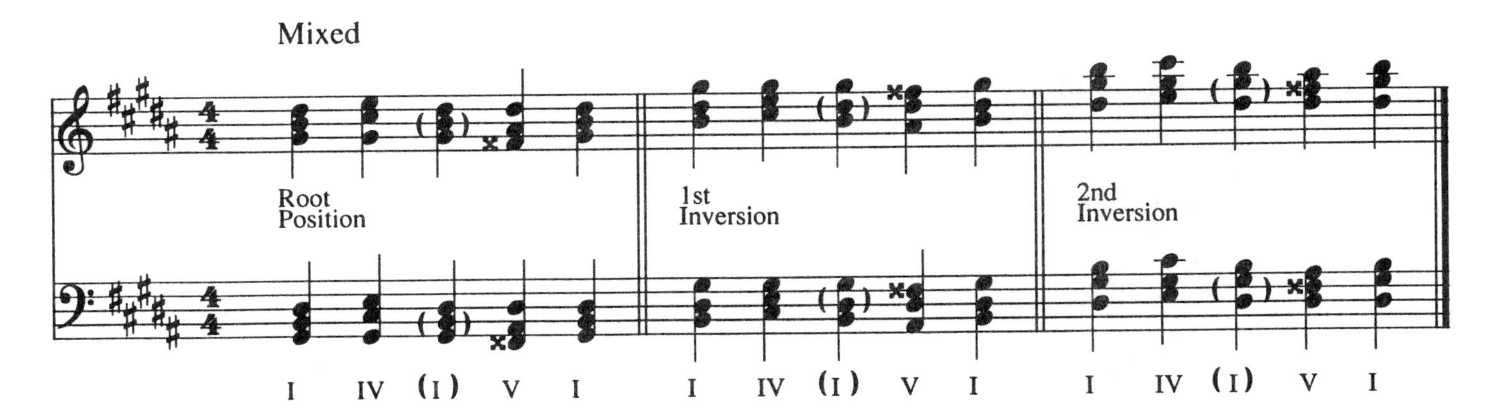
Mixed
Root Position
1st Inversion
2nd Inversion
I IV (I) V I
I IV (I) V I
I IV (I) V I

G Sharp Melodic Minor Scale (2 Octave)

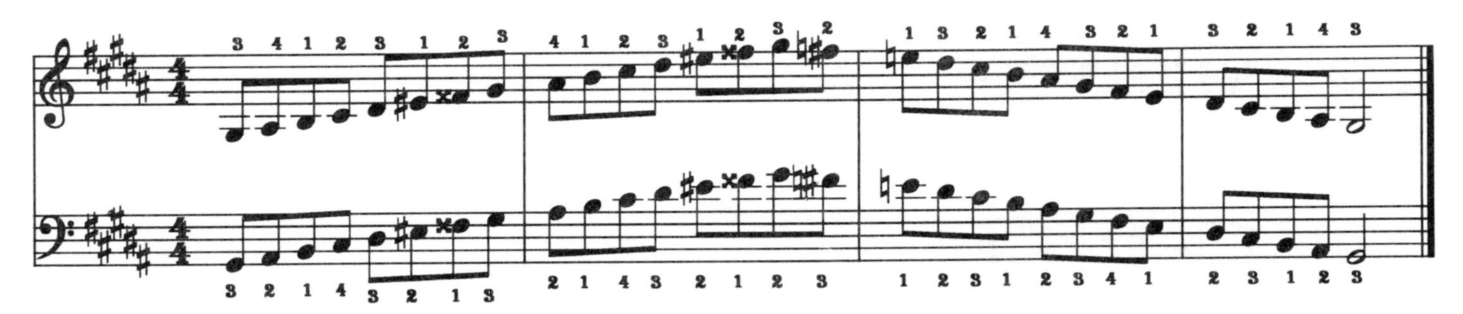

D Minor

(Relative Minor to F Major)

D Harmonic Minor Scale (1 Octave)

D Harmonic Minor Scale (2 Octave)

D Minor Arpeggio (1 Octave)   D Minor Arpeggio (2 Octaves)

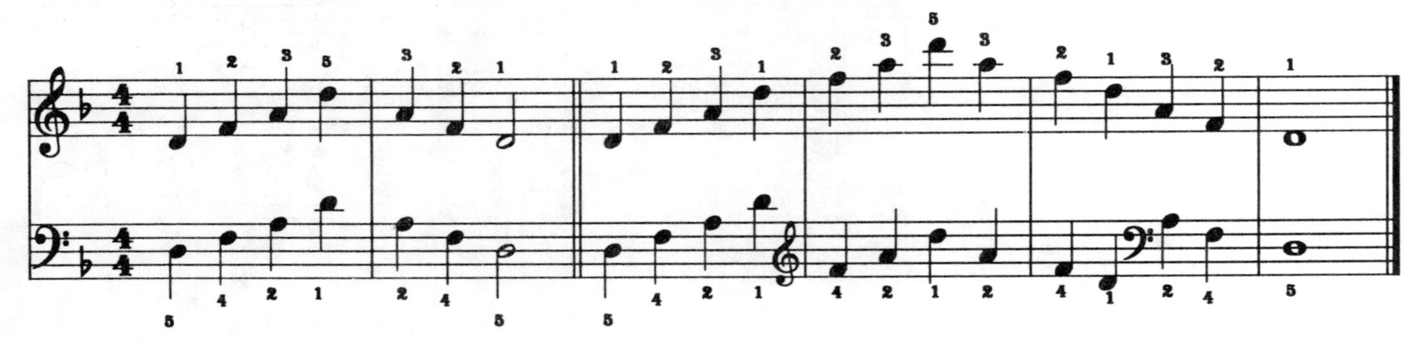

D Minor Arpeggios In Inversions

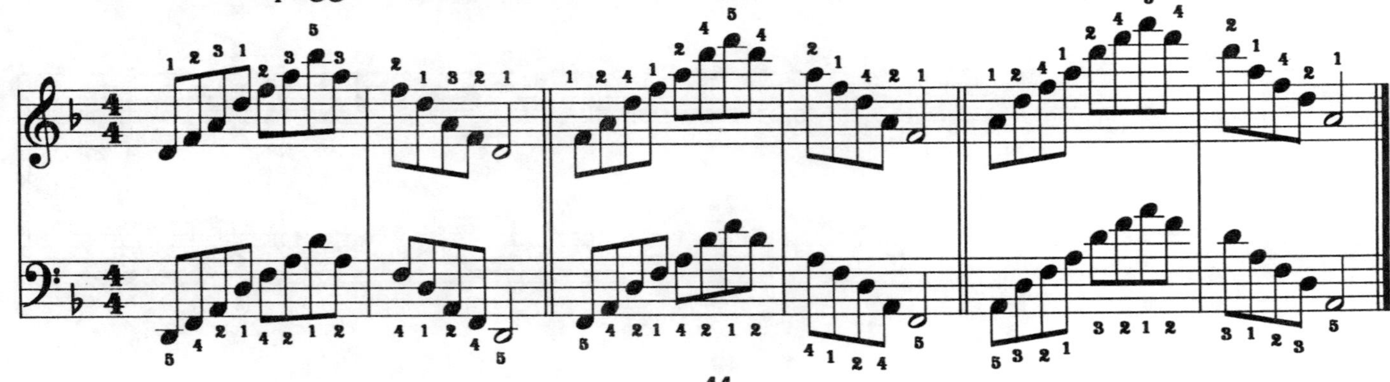

Inversions of Principal Chords of D Minor

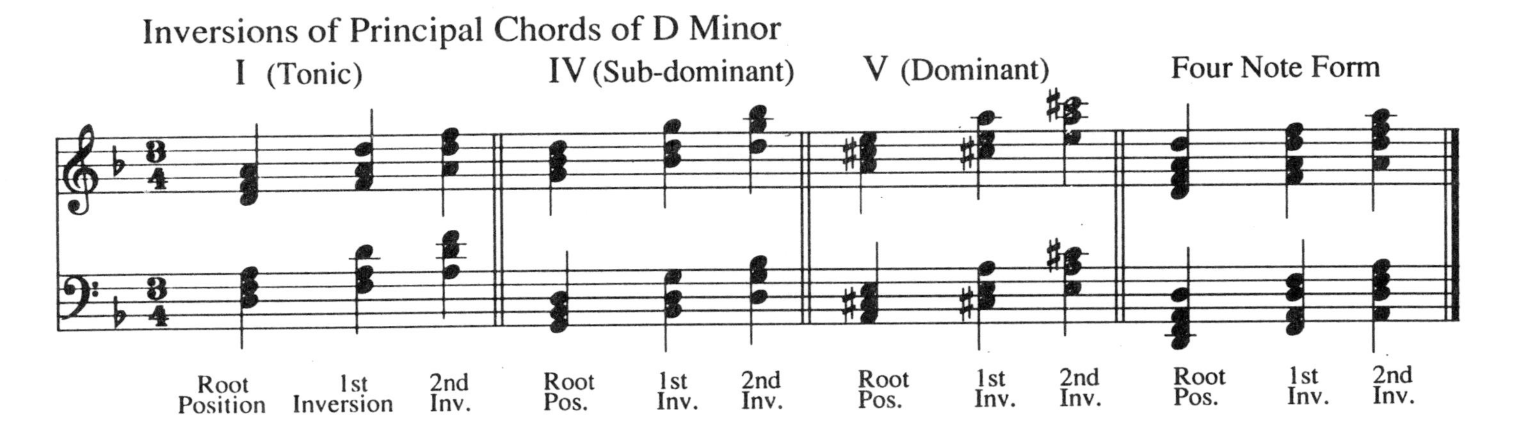
I (Tonic)
IV (Sub-dominant)
V (Dominant)
Four Note Form
Root Position
1st Inversion
2nd Inv.
Root Pos.
1st Inv.
2nd Inv.
Root Pos.
1st Inv.
2nd Inv.
Root Pos.
1st Inv.
2nd Inv.

Cadences In D Minor

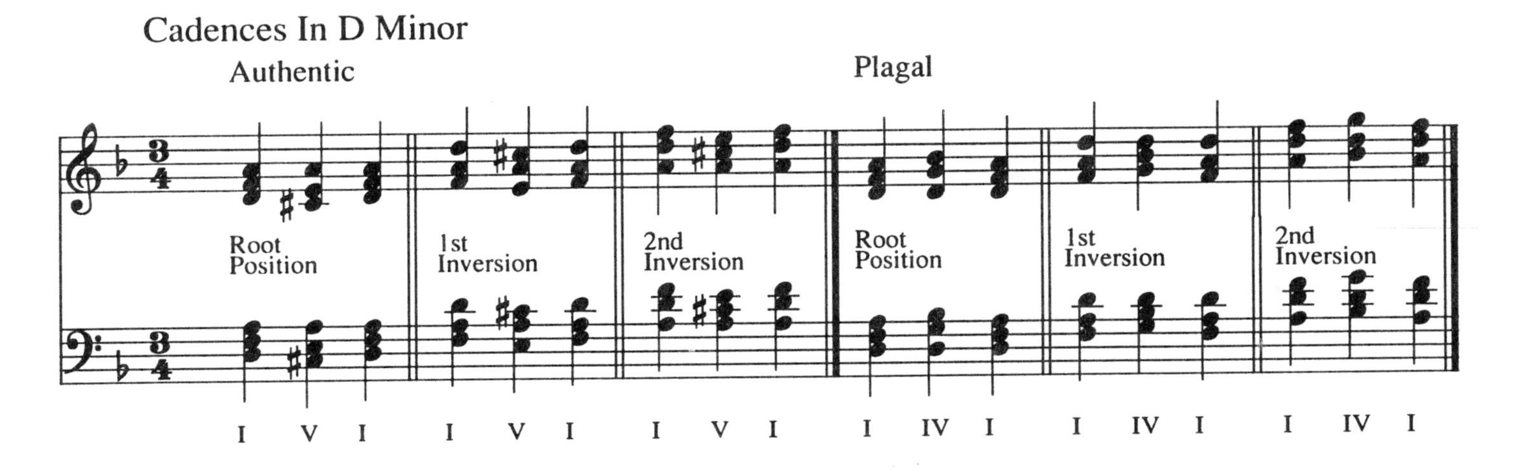
Authentic
Plagal
Root Position
1st Inversion
2nd Inversion
Root Position
1st Inversion
2nd Inversion
I V I
I V I
I V I
I IV I
I IV I
I IV I

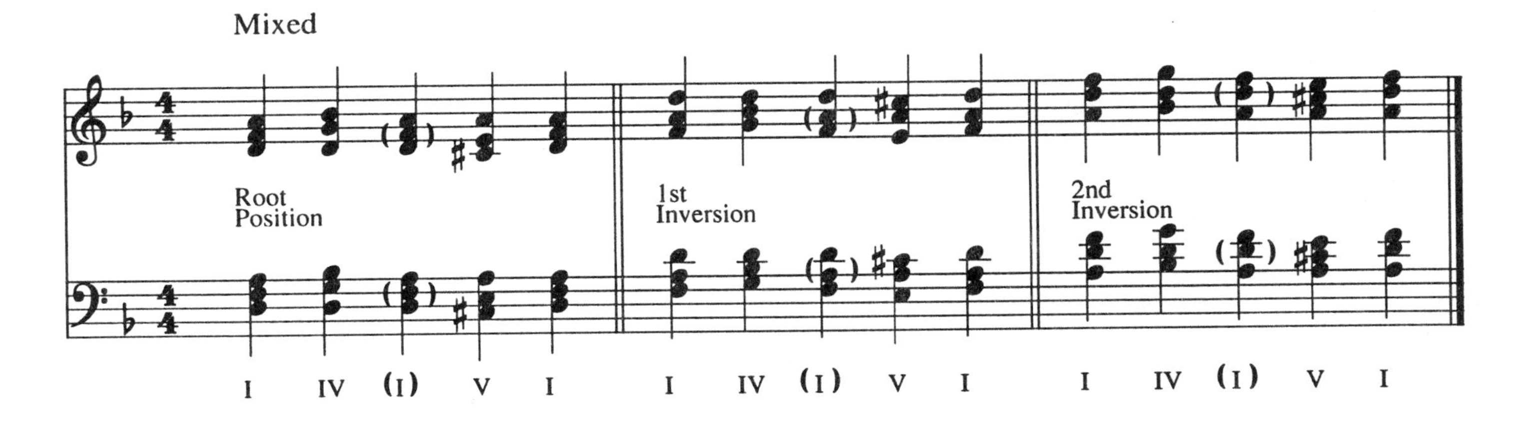
Mixed
Root Position
1st Inversion
2nd Inversion
I IV (I) V I
I IV (I) V I
I IV (I) V I

D Melodic Minor Scale (2 Octave)

G Minor

(Relative Minor to B Flat Major)

G Harmonic Minor Scale (1 Octave)

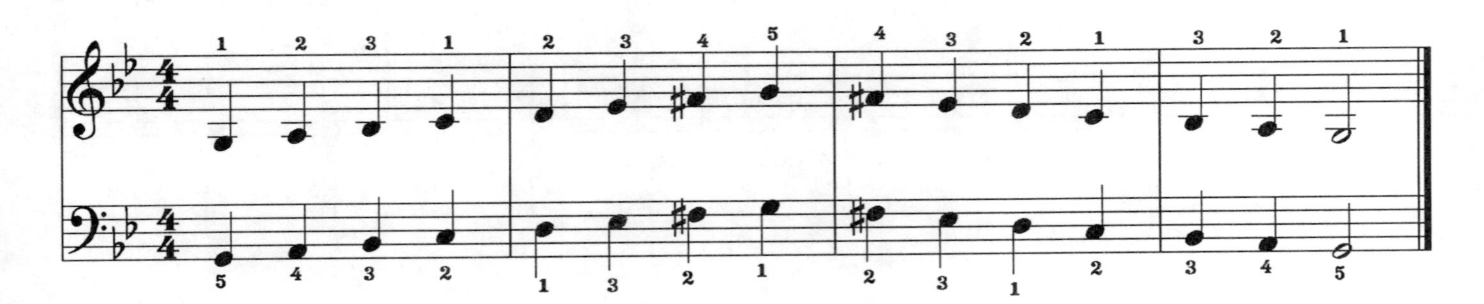

G Harmonic Minor Scale (2 Octave)

G Minor Arpeggio (1 Octave)   G Minor Arpeggio (2 Octaves)

G Minor Arpeggios In Inversions

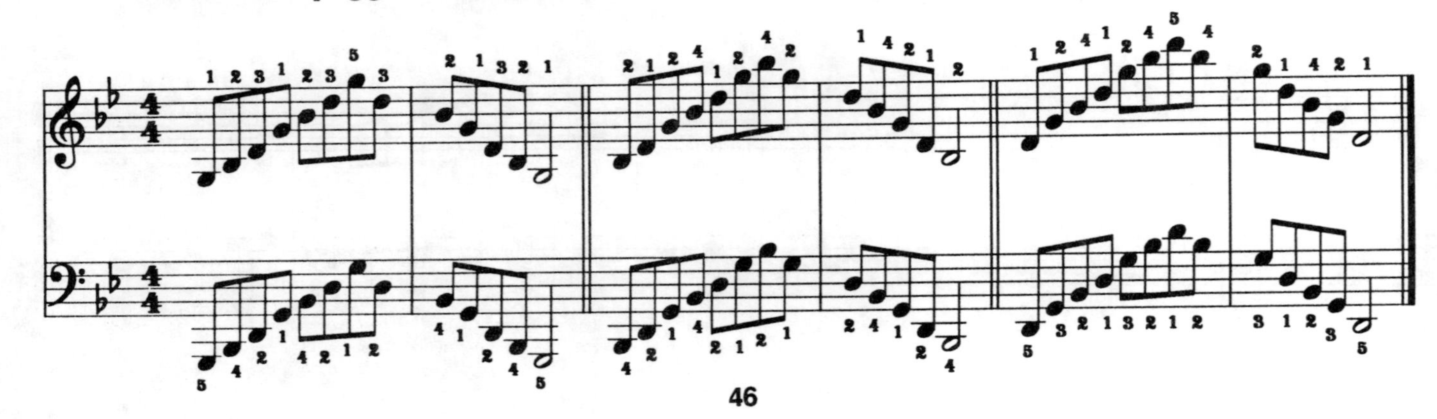

Inversions of Principal Chords of G Minor

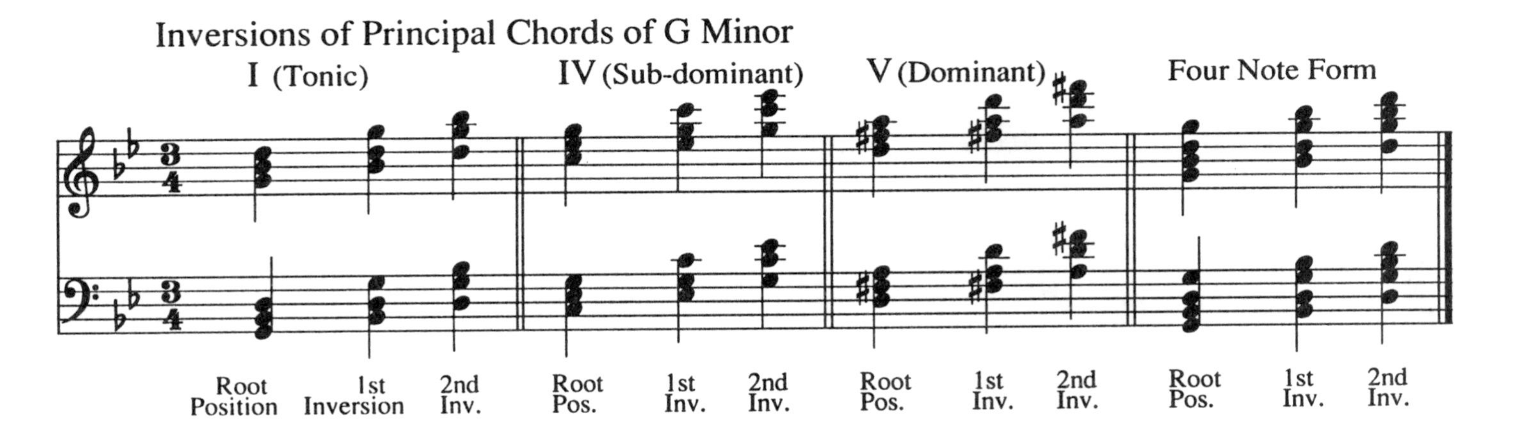
I (Tonic)
IV (Sub-dominant)
V (Dominant)
Four Note Form
Root Position
1st Inversion
2nd Inv.
Root Pos.
1st Inv.
2nd Inv.
Root Pos.
1st Inv.
2nd Inv.
Root Pos.
1st Inv.
2nd Inv.

Cadences In G Minor

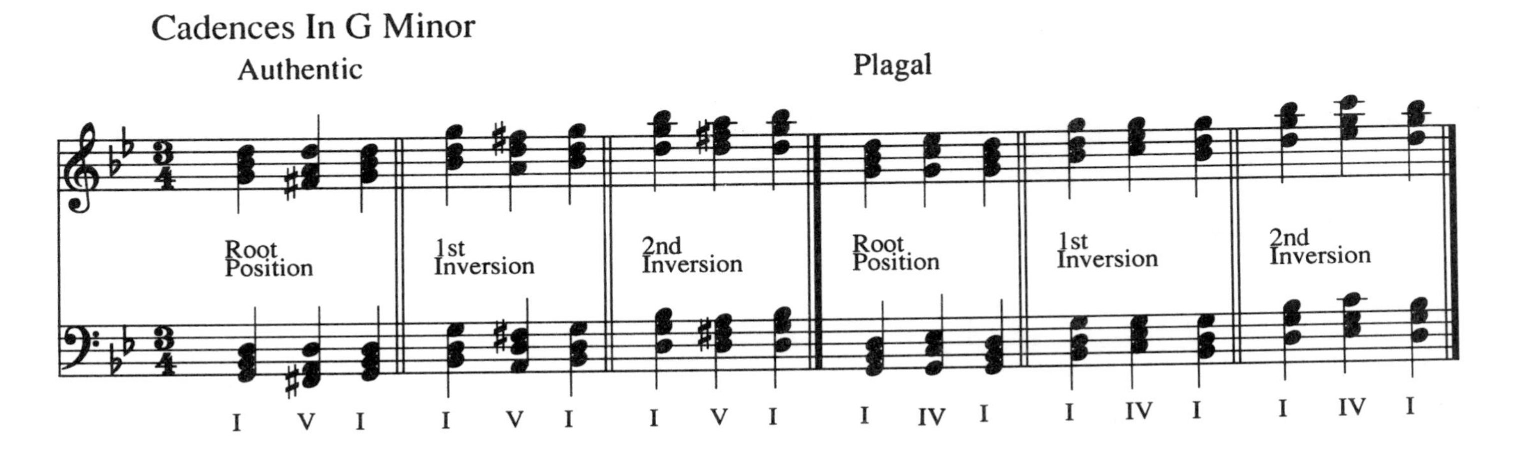
Authentic
Plagal
Root Position
1st Inversion
2nd Inversion
Root Position
1st Inversion
2nd Inversion
I V I
I V I
I V I
I IV I
I IV I
I IV I

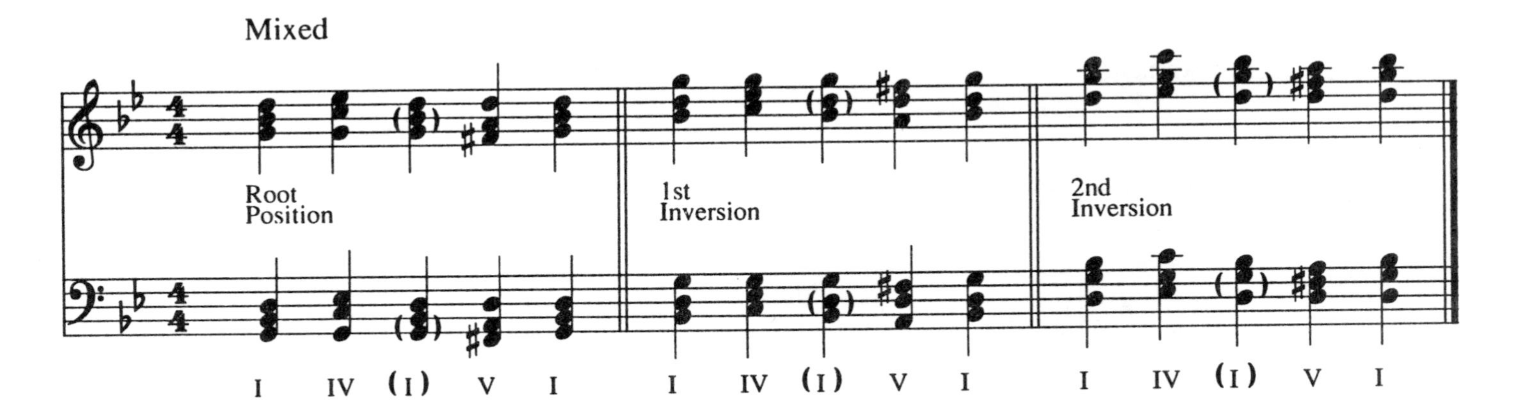
Mixed
Root Position
1st Inversion
2nd Inversion
I IV (I) V I
I IV (I) V I
I IV (I) V I

G Melodic Minor Scale (2 Octave)

C Minor
(Relative Minor to E Flat Major

C Harmonic Minor Scale (1 Octave)

C Harmonic Minor Scale (2 Octave)

C Minor Arpeggio (1 Octave) C Minor Arpeggio (2 Octaves)

C Minor Arpeggios In Inversions

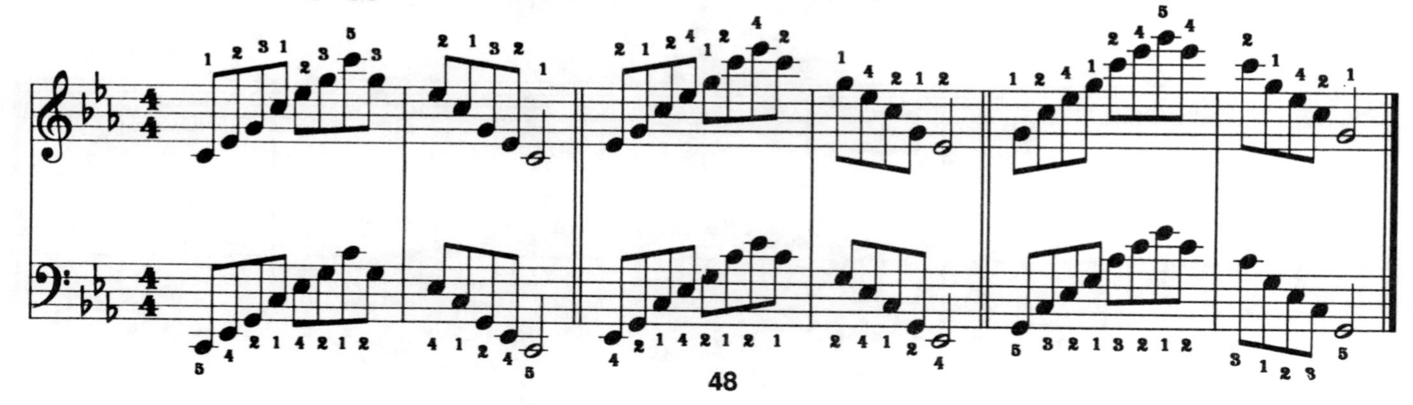

Inversions of Principal Chords of C Minor

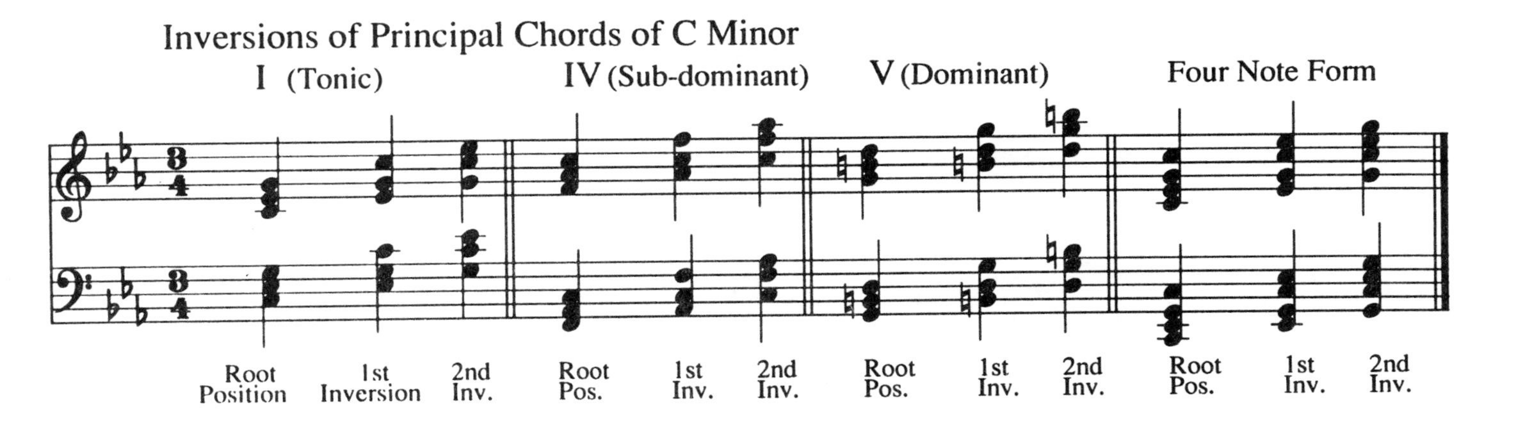
I (Tonic)
IV (Sub-dominant)
V (Dominant)
Four Note Form
Root Position
1st Inversion
2nd Inv.
Root Pos.
1st Inv.
2nd Inv.
Root Pos.
1st Inv.
2nd Inv.
Root Pos.
1st Inv.
2nd Inv.

Cadences In C Minor

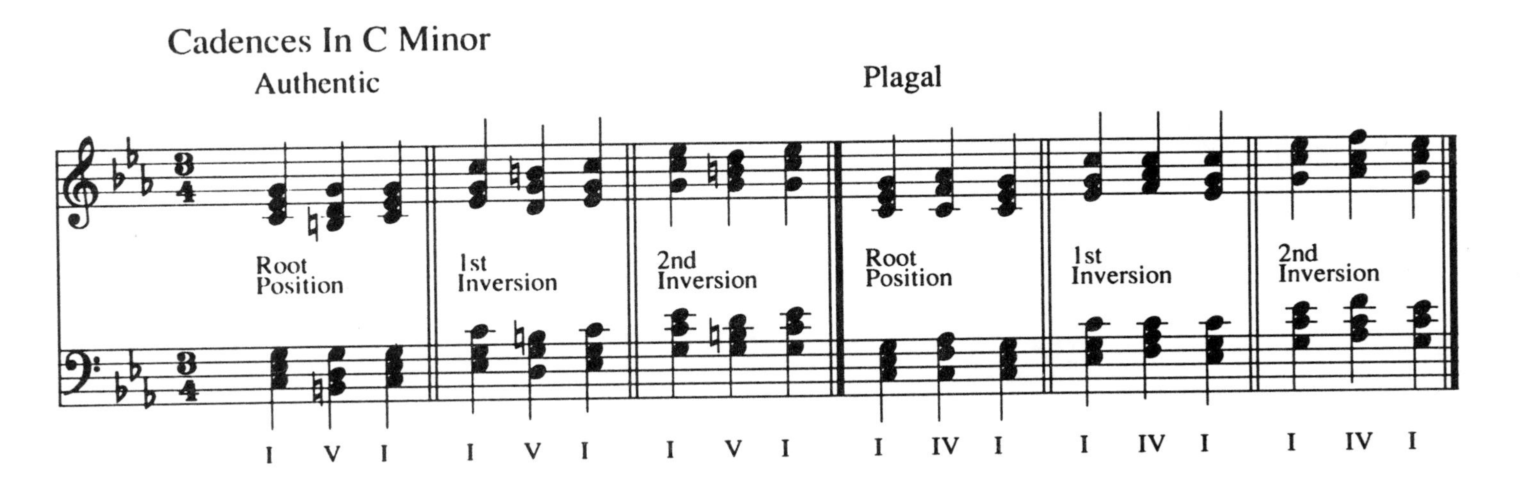
Authentic
Plagal
Root Position
1st Inversion
2nd Inversion
Root Position
1st Inversion
2nd Inversion
I V I
I V I
I V I
I IV I
I IV I
I IV I

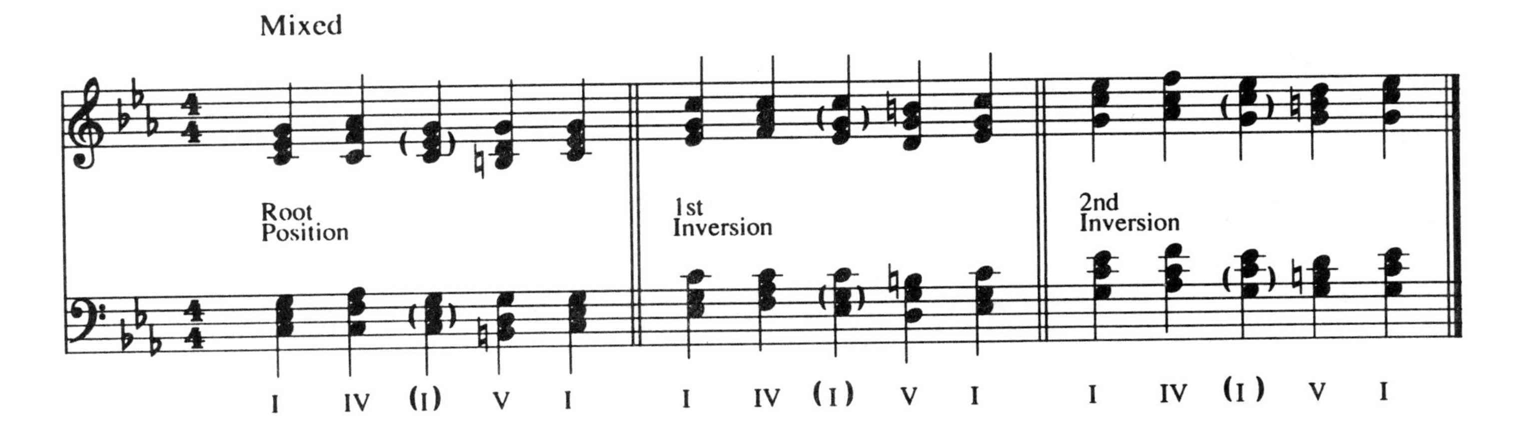
Mixed
Root Position
1st Inversion
2nd Inversion
I IV (I) V I
I IV (I) V I
I IV (I) V I

C Melodic Minor Scale (2 Octave)

F Minor

(Relative Minor to A Flat Major)

F Harmonic Minor Scale (1 Octave)

F Harmonic Minor Scale (2 Octave)

F Minor Arpeggio (1 Octave)   F Minor Arpeggio (2 Octaves)

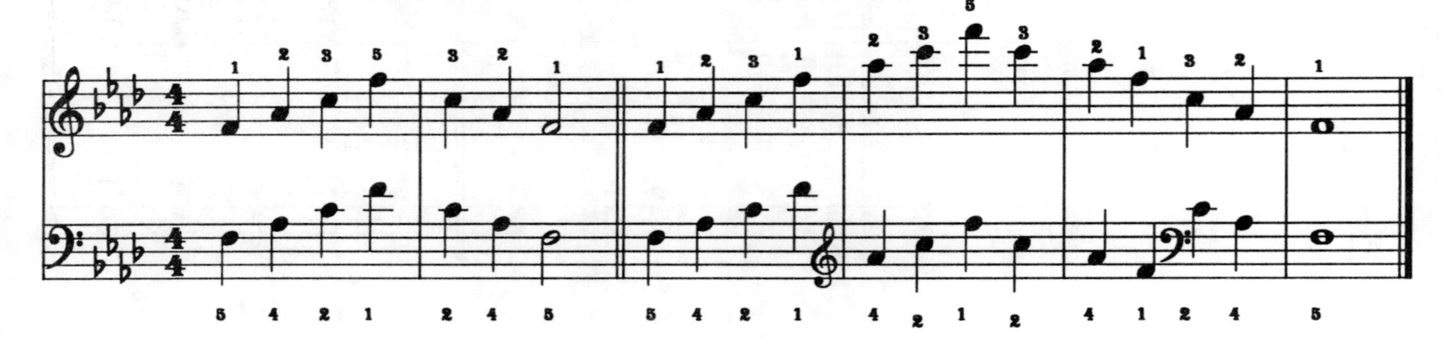

F Minor Arpeggios In Inversions

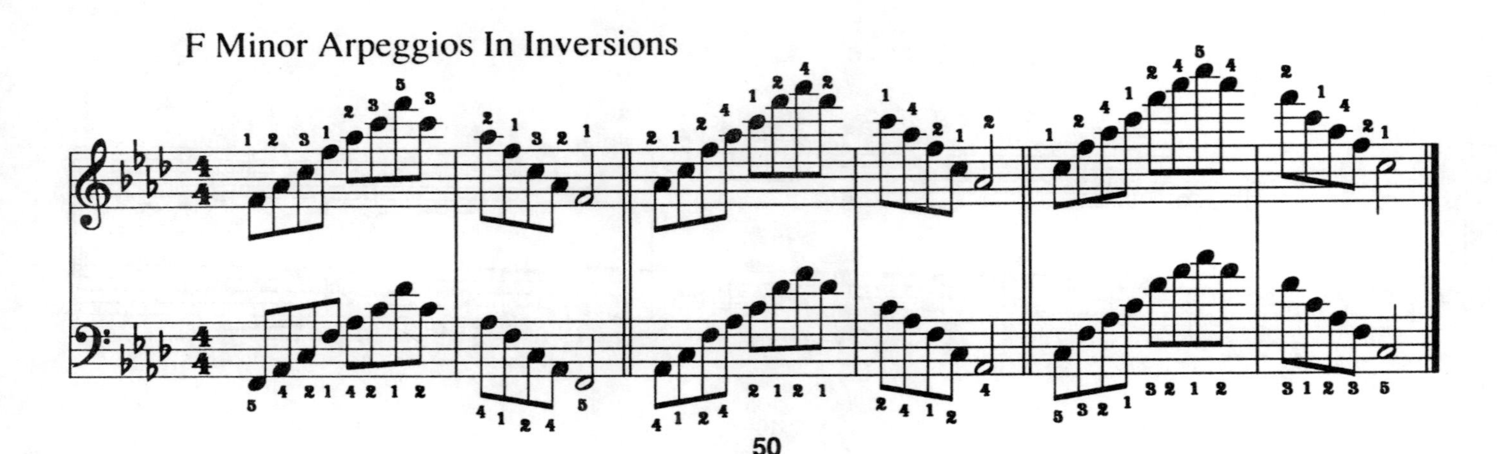

Inversions of Principal Chords of F Minor

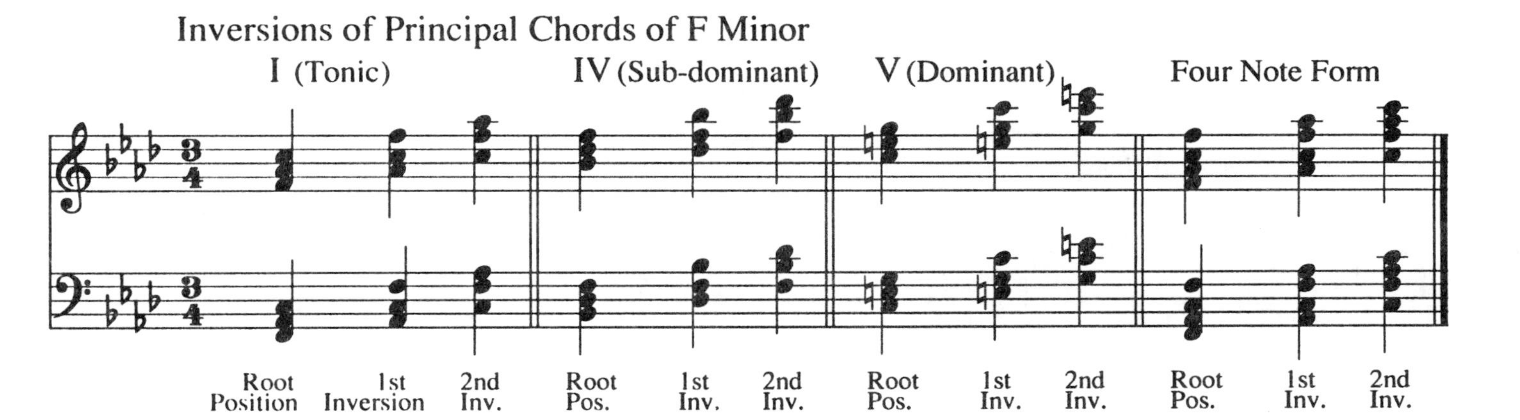

I (Tonic)
IV (Sub-dominant)
V (Dominant)
Four Note Form
Root Position
1st Inversion
2nd Inv.
Root Pos.
1st Inv.
2nd Inv.
Root Pos.
1st Inv.
2nd Inv.
Root Pos.
1st Inv.
2nd Inv.

Cadences In F Minor

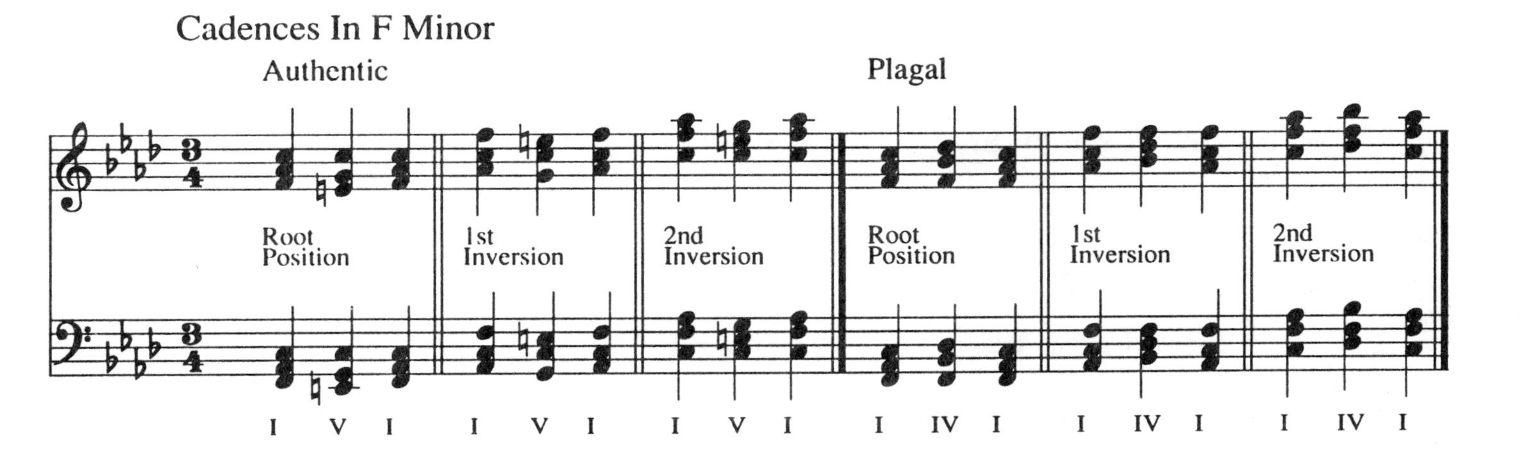

Authentic
Plagal
Root Position
1st Inversion
2nd Inversion
Root Position
1st Inversion
2nd Inversion
I V I
I V I
I V I
I IV I
I IV I
I IV I

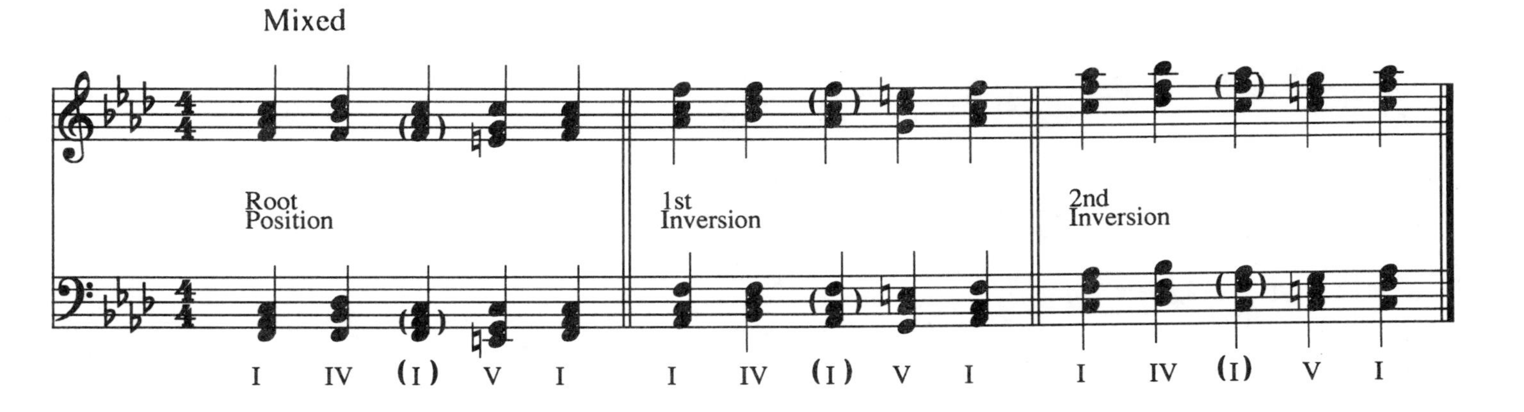

Mixed
Root Position
1st Inversion
2nd Inversion
I IV (I) V I
I IV (I) V I
I IV (I) V I

F Melodic Minor Scale (2 Octave)

B Flat Minor
(Relative Minor to D Flat Major)

B♭ Harmonic Minor Scale (1 Octave)

B♭ Harmonic Minor Scale (2 Octave)

B♭ Minor Arpeggio (1 Octave)   B♭ Minor Arpeggio (2 Octaves)

B♭ Minor Arpeggios In Inversions

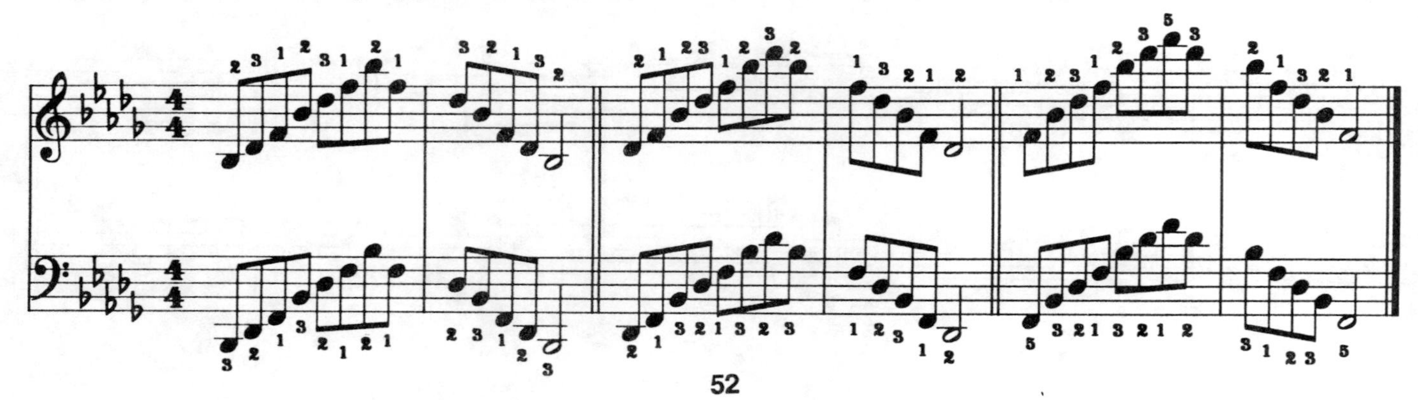

Inversions of Principal Chords of B♭ Minor

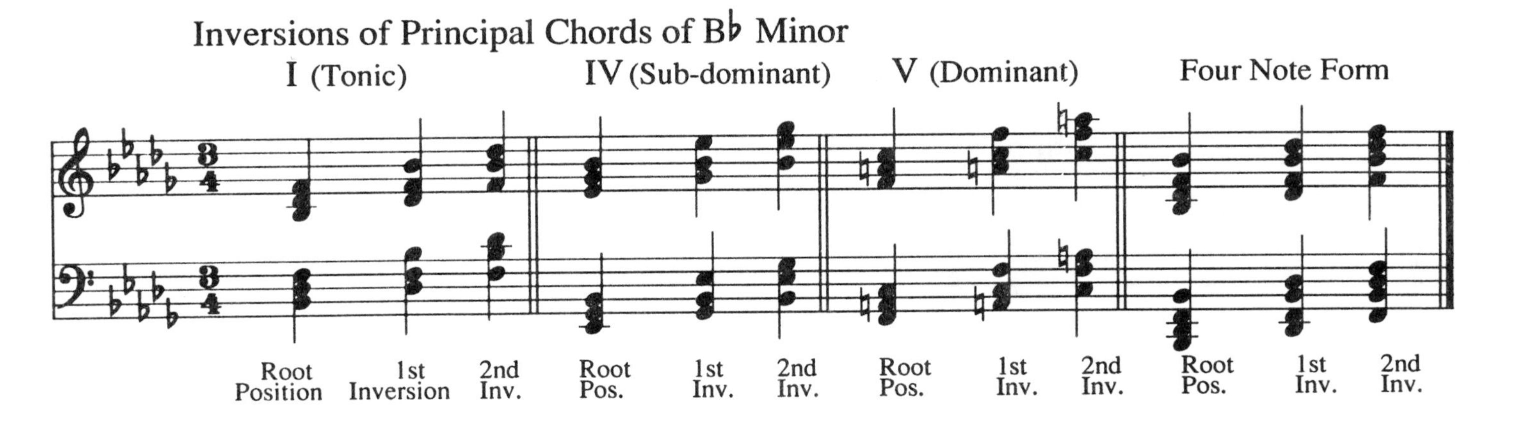
I (Tonic)
IV (Sub-dominant)
V (Dominant)
Four Note Form
Root Position
1st Inversion
2nd Inv.
Root Pos.
1st Inv.
2nd Inv.
Root Pos.
1st Inv.
2nd Inv.
Root Pos.
1st Inv.
2nd Inv.

Cadences In B♭ Minor

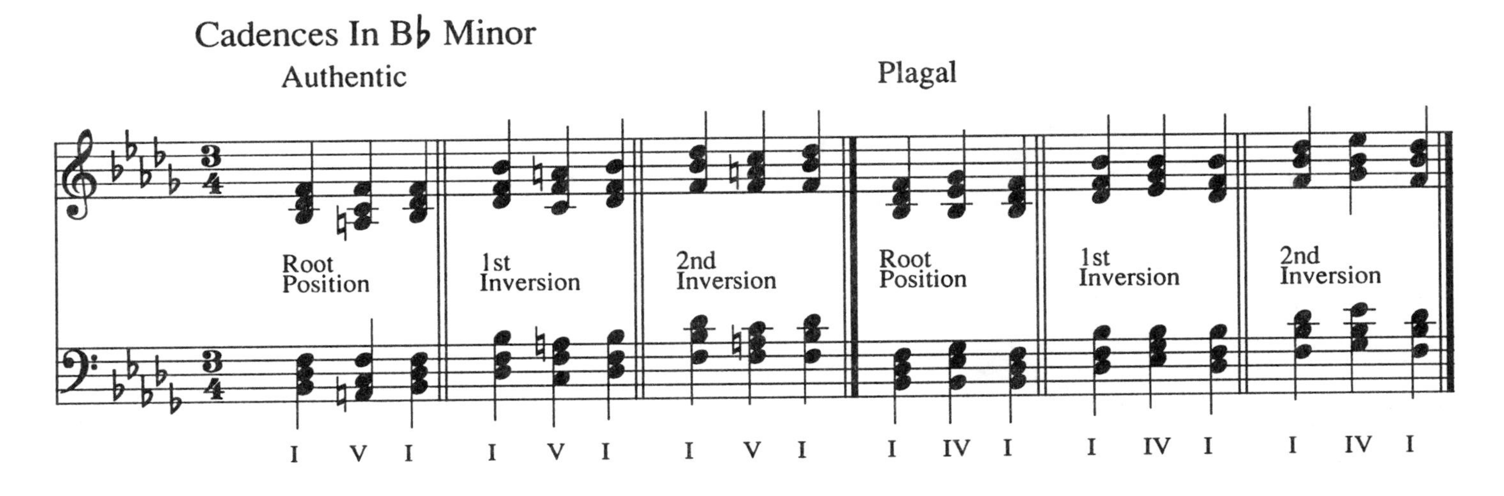
Authentic
Plagal
Root Position
1st Inversion
2nd Inversion
Root Position
1st Inversion
2nd Inversion
I V I
I V I
I V I
I IV I
I IV I
I IV I

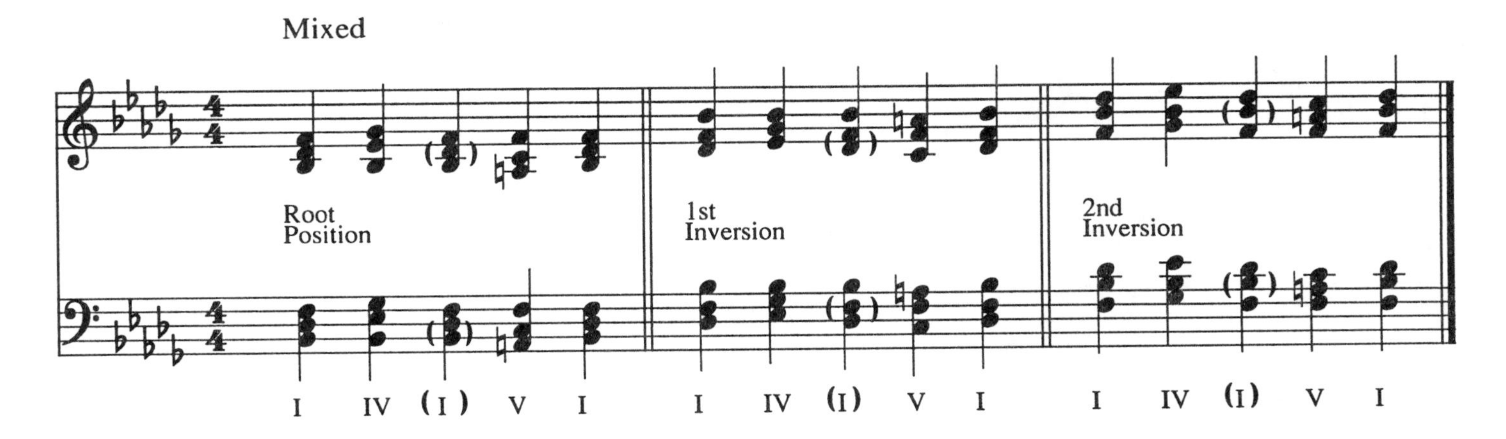
Mixed
Root Position
1st Inversion
2nd Inversion
I IV (I) V I
I IV (I) V I
I IV (I) V I

B Flat Melodic Minor Scale (2 Octave)

E Flat Minor

(Relative Minor to G Flat Major)

E♭ Harmonic Minor Scale (1 Octave)

E♭ Harmonic Minor Scale (2 Octave)

E♭ Minor Arpeggio (1 Octave) E♭ Minor Arpeggio (2 Octaves)

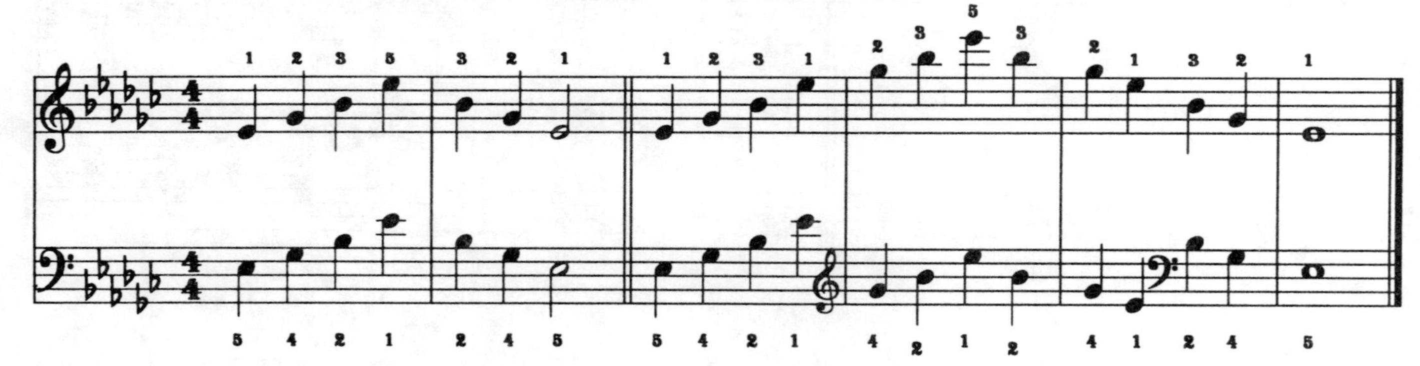

E♭ Minor Arpeggios In Inversions

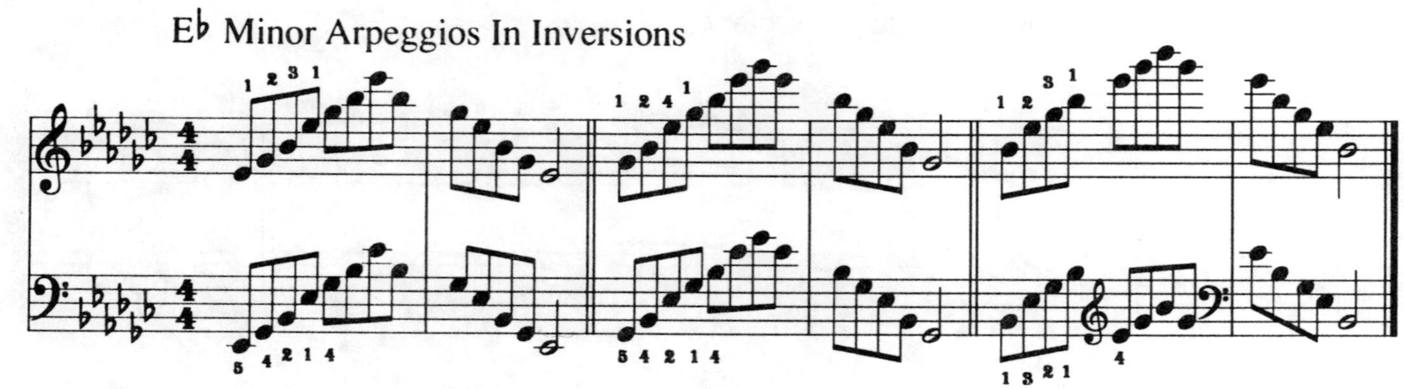

Inversions of Principal Chords of E♭ Minor

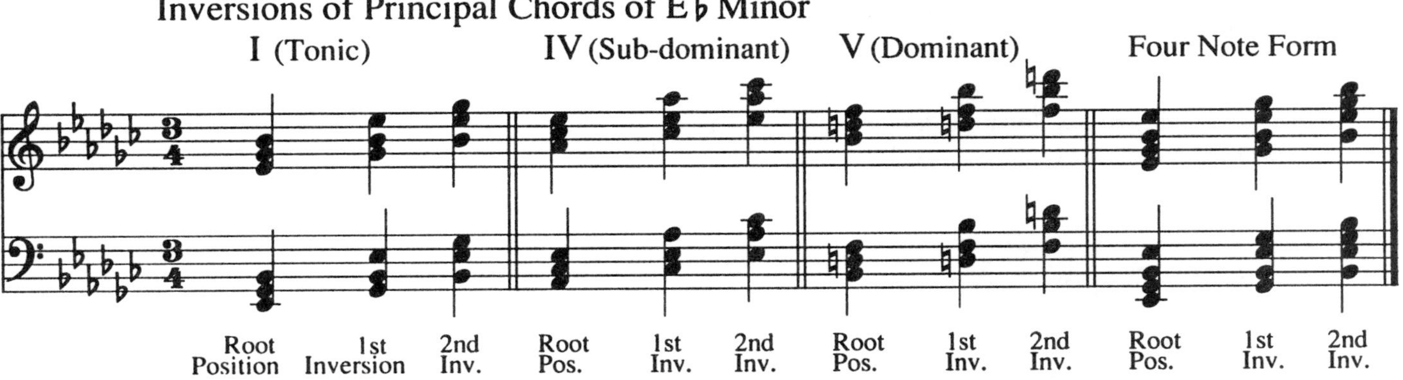
I (Tonic)
IV (Sub-dominant)
V (Dominant)
Four Note Form
Root Position
1st Inversion
2nd Inv.
Root Pos.
1st Inv.
2nd Inv.
Root Pos.
1st Inv.
2nd Inv.
Root Pos.
1st Inv.
2nd Inv.

Cadences In E♭ Minor

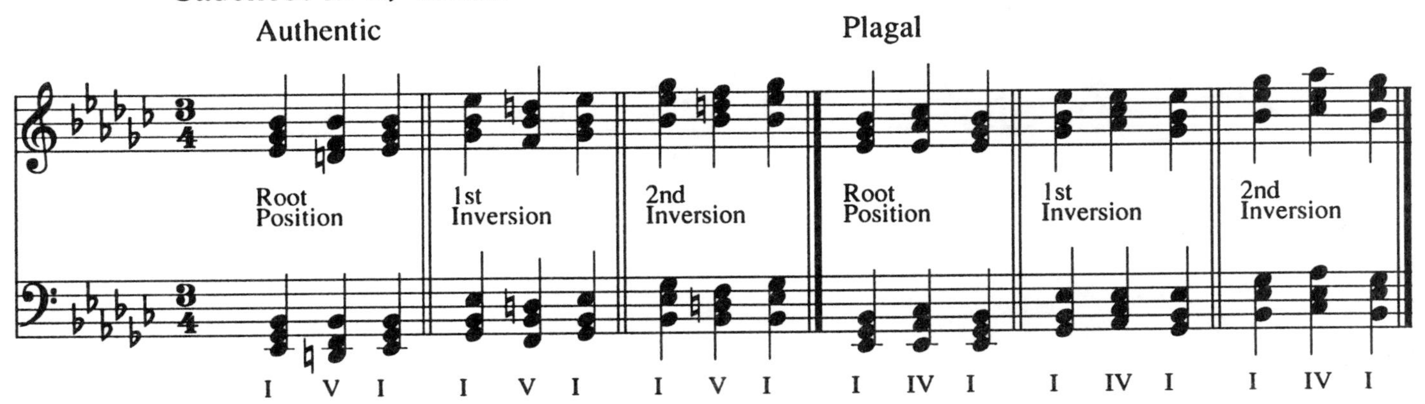
Authentic
Plagal
Root Position
1st Inversion
2nd Inversion
Root Position
1st Inversion
2nd Inversion
I V I
I V I
I V I
I IV I
I IV I
I IV I

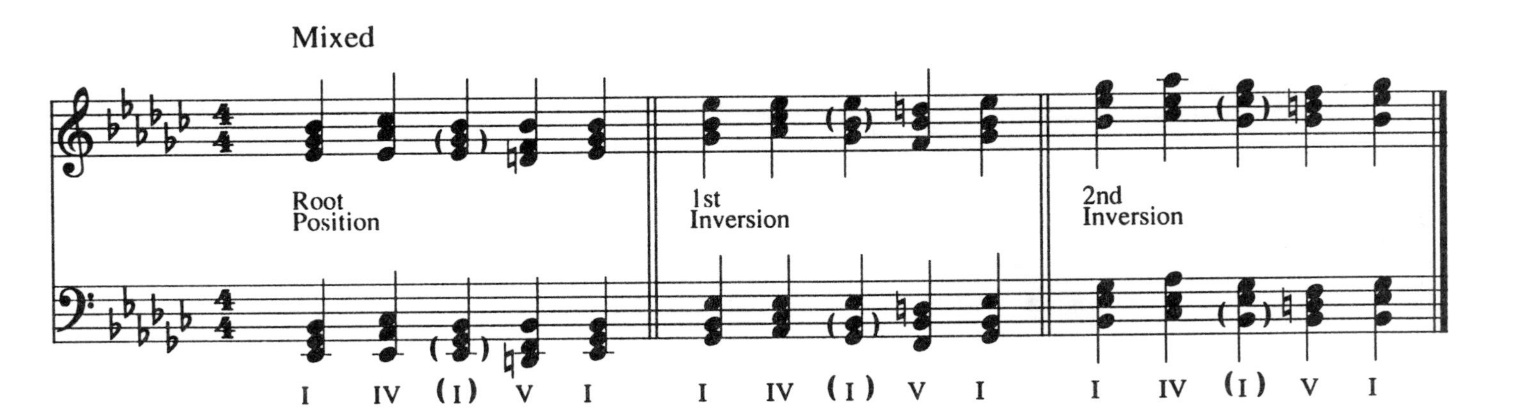
Mixed
Root Position
1st Inversion
2nd Inversion
I IV (I) V I
I IV (I) V I
I IV (I) V I

E Flat Melodic Minor Scale (2 Octave)

Diminished Seventh Chords and Arpeggios

The Diminished Seventh Chord is built on the seventh step of any major or minor scale. It consists of three minor thirds and may be inverted from root positions through 1st, 2nd and 3rd inversions. The Diminished Seventh Chord may also be thought of as a Diminished Triad plus a minor third.

Key of C (Major Or Minor)

Key of G (Major Or Minor)

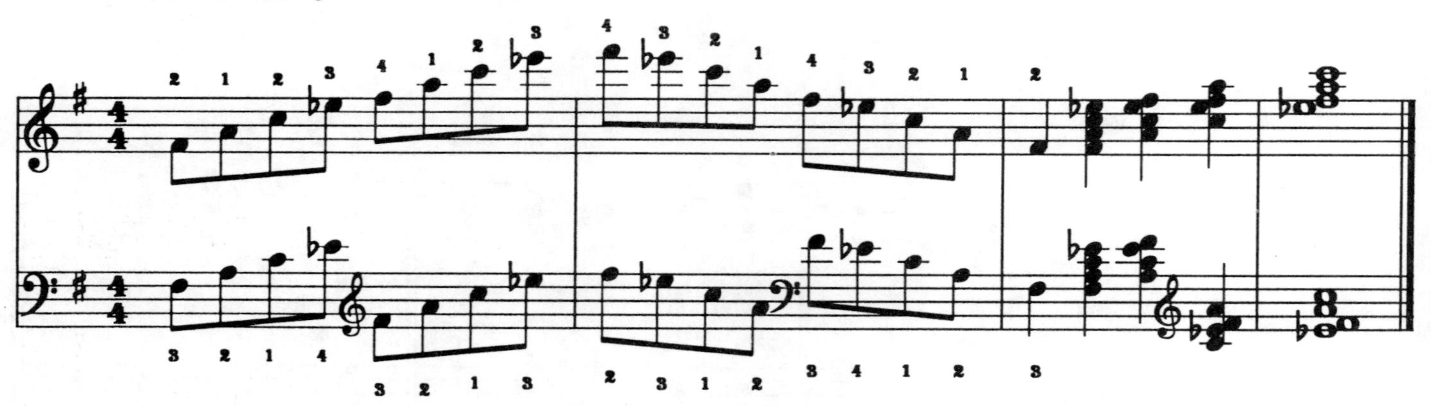

Key of D (Major Or Minor)

Key of A (Major Or Minor)

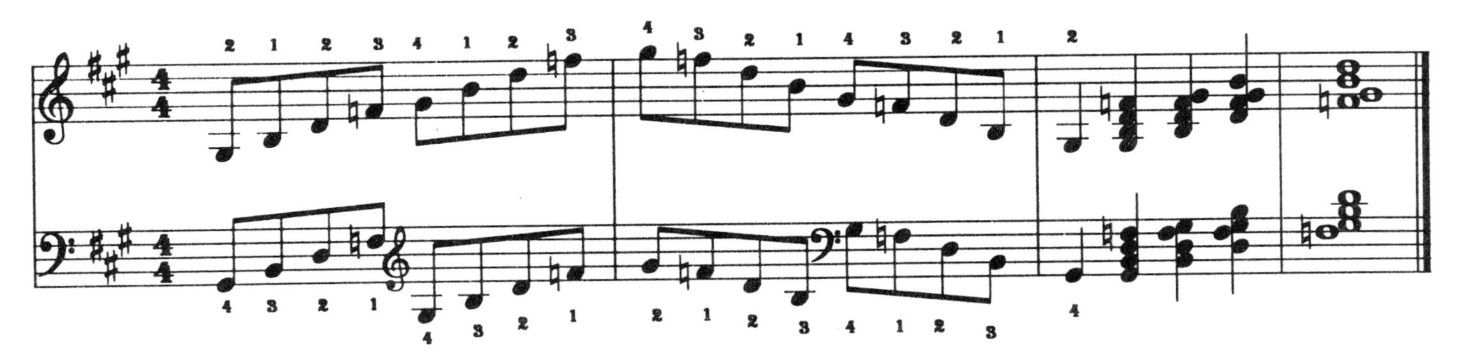

Key of E (Major Or Minor)

Key of B (Major Or Minor)

Key of F Sharp (Major Or Minor)

Key of F (Major Or Minor)

Key of B Flat (Major Or Minor)

Key of E Flat (Major Or Minor)

Key of A Flat (Major Or Minor)

Key of D Flat (Major Or Minor)

Chromatic Scale

The Chromatic Scale consists of the 12 different tones, all at the distance of one half step.

Chromatic Scale (1 Octave)

Chromatic Scale (2 Octave)

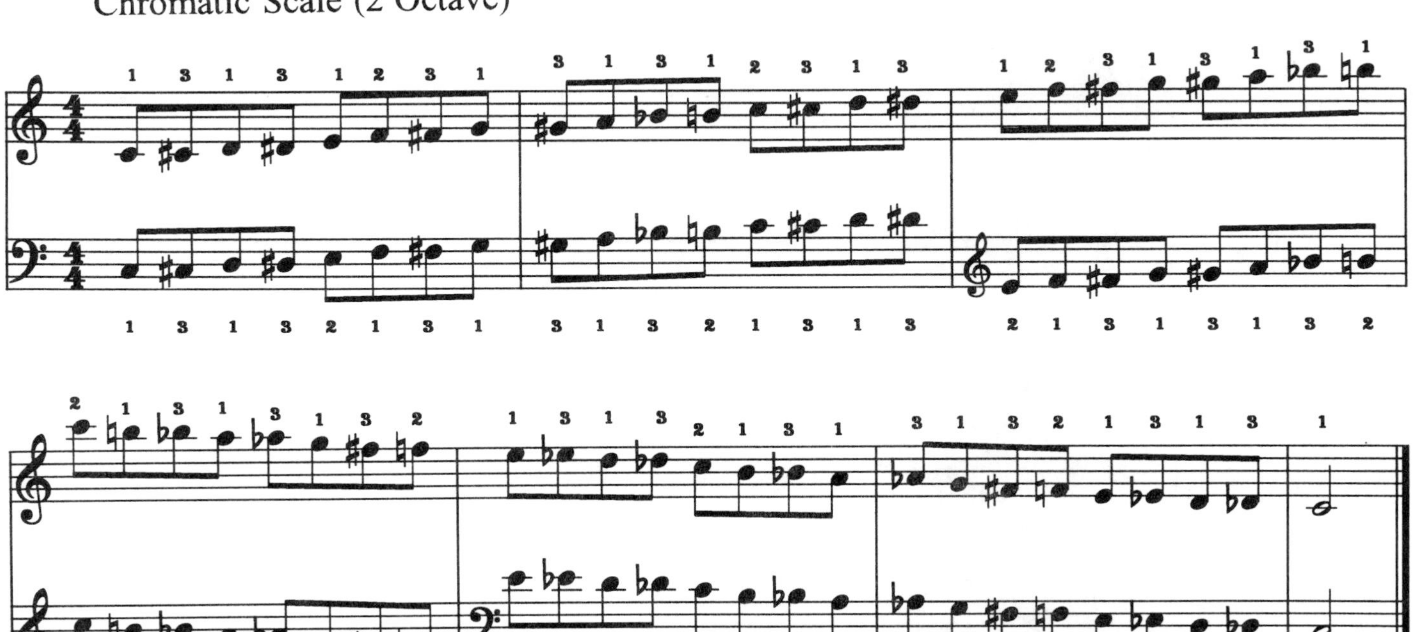

Chord Chart

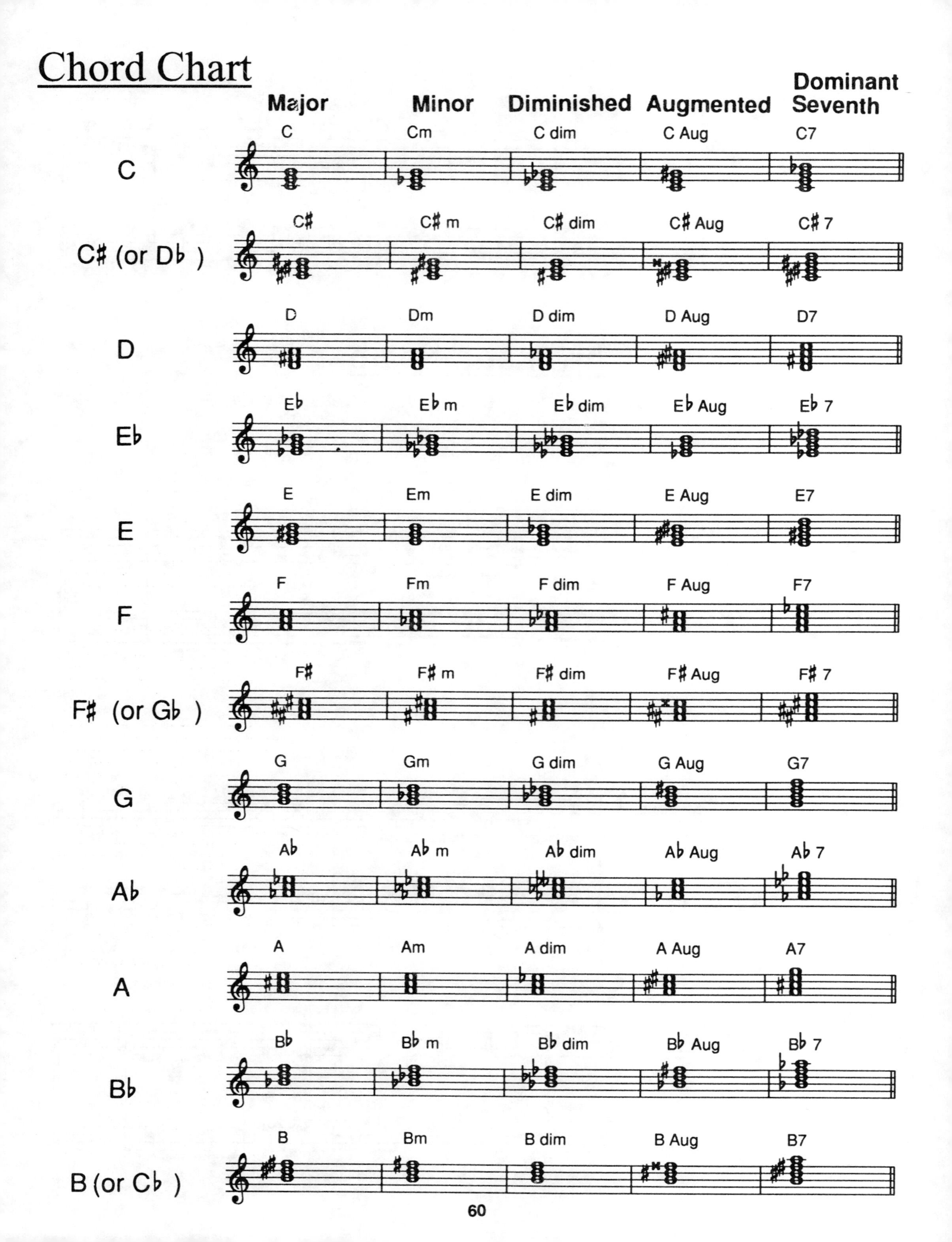

Major
Minor
Diminished
Augmented
Dominant Seventh
C
Cm
C dim
C Aug
C7
C
C♯
C♯ m
C♯ dim
C♯ Aug
C♯ 7
C♯ (or D♭)
D
Dm
D dim
D Aug
D7
D
E♭
E♭ m
E♭ dim
E♭ Aug
E♭ 7
E♭
E
Em
E dim
E Aug
E7
E
F
Fm
F dim
F Aug
F7
F
F♯
F♯ m
F♯ dim
F♯ Aug
F♯ 7
F♯ (or G♭)
G
Gm
G dim
G Aug
G7
G
A♭
A♭ m
A♭ dim
A♭ Aug
A♭ 7
A♭
A
Am
A dim
A Aug
A7
A
B♭
B♭ m
B♭ dim
B♭ Aug
B♭ 7
B♭
B
Bm
B dim
B Aug
B7
B (or C♭)

Basic Keyboard Chords

Basic
Keyboard Chords
Popular chords in
diagram form with
accompaniment patterns

Easy to read chord diagrams and notation. Includes left hand rhythms, chord construction, and inversions.

___$4.95 (OEP040)

Shown Actual Size

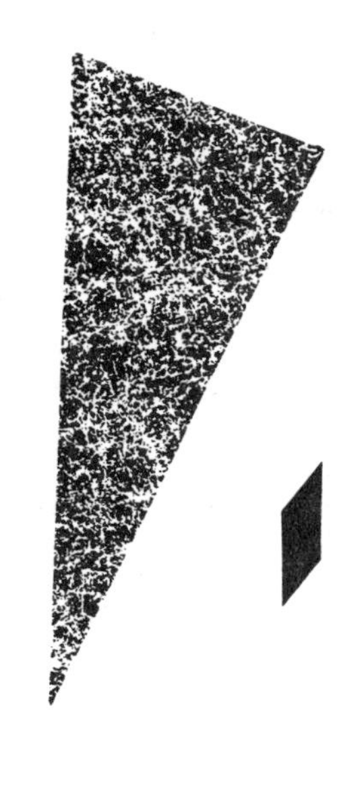

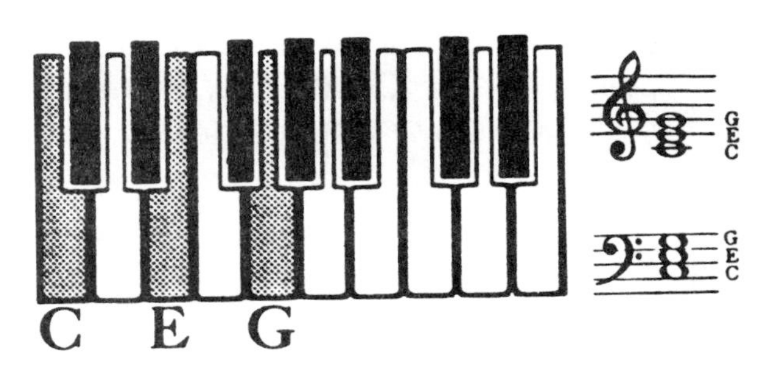

C
C E G
G E C
G E C

Available At
Your Favorite Music Store

Available at your favorite music store

Basic
Keyboard
Chords
Classic
Easy Piano
Children's Songs
First
Teacher's Classics
Hanon Complete
The Virtuoso Pianist

BASIC KEYBOARD CHORDS:
Easy to read chord diagrams and notation. Includes left hand rhythms, chord construction and inversions.
___$4.95 (OEP040)

CLASSIC CHILDREN'S SONGS:
Features fresh easy piano arrangements of over 70 traditional childhood favorites with clever illustrations geared to keep the early player interested and entertained.
___$10.95 (OEP111)

FIRST TEACHER'S CLASSICS:
Simplified arrangements of Fur Elise, Clair De Lune, Ode To Joy, Jesu, Joy Of Man's Desiring, Minuet, Largo, Romeo & Juliet and much more.
___$7.95 (OEP233)

HANON COMPLETE:
A new edition of the classic bible for pianists.
___$6.95 (OEP050)

Elegant Wedding Classics
Hymn Favorites

CHERISHED HYMN FAVORITES:
Tri-chord arrangements of Amazing Grace, The Holy City, Kum Ba Yah, The Palms, Rock Of Ages, He's Got The Whole World In His Hands, Morning Has Broken, and many others.
___$7.95 (OEP103)

ELEGANT WEDDING CLASSICS:
Time-honored favorites for the celebration of love. Over 15 traditional wedding standards, beautifully arranged for piano are included in the sure-hit songbook. Includes Ave Maria (Bach & Schubert), Trumpet Voluntary, Wedding March, Bridal Chorus, Canon In D, Morning Has Broken, Ode To Joy, Jesu, Joy Of Man's Desiring, and many more.
___$9.95 (JT51)

JT
PUBLICATIONS

P.O. BOX 9368
PEORIA, IL 61612